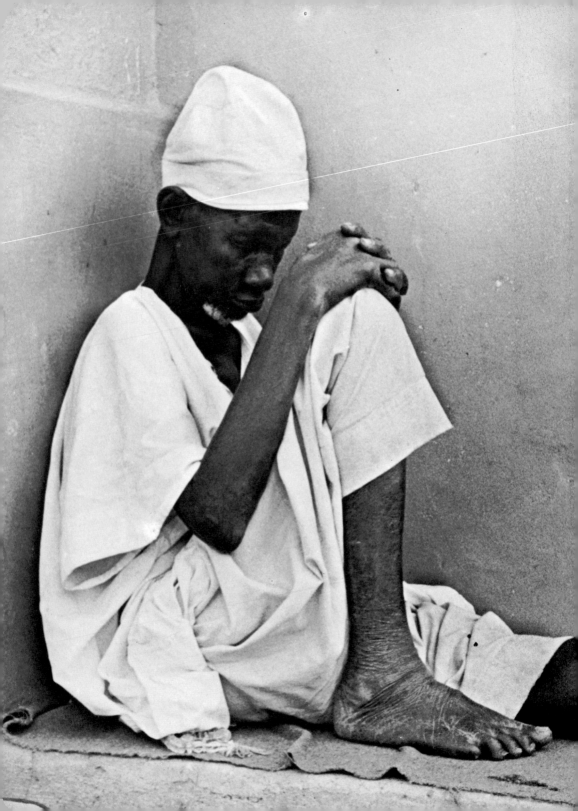

Thoughtshapes

Barry Maybury

OXFORD UNIVERSITY PRESS 1972

Oxford University Press, Ely House, London W.1

GLASGOW NEW YORK TORONTO MELBOURNE WELLINGTON
CAPE TOWN SALISBURY IBADAN NAIROBI DAR ES SALAAM LUSAKA
ADDIS ABABA BOMBAY CALCUTTA MADRAS KARACHI LAHORE DACCA
KUALA LUMPUR SINGAPORE HONG KONG TOKYO

By the same author:
Wordscapes (Oxford University Press) — a companion
collection of prose and verse
Creative Writing for Juniors (B. T. Batsford Ltd. London)

Photoset by BAS Printers Ltd., Wallop, Hampshire
and printed in Great Britain by
Hazell, Watson and Viney Ltd., Aylesbury

Contents

Strange worlds

Machines that die

All is quiet now the place is still.
The drilling machine a minute ago
Spinning and screaming through bright metal
Is still as if touched by a witch's wand.
No more does the lathe turn its ugly chuck,
And the wicked looking tool with its
Curled lip has disengaged itself
From the flying steel.
Spanners, hammers, wrenches and oily rags
Are in disarray along silent empty benches.
A workman's hat hangs on a hook,
Its peak pointing down to a broken casting.
The lights are now off,
And the only live occupants—
Two mice running along a twisted chair.

STEPHEN HART, aged 13

The furnace

A maze of rusted pipes twist, coil and bend around an enormous room. A complicated mass of deafening machinery working day and night to produce electricity. The odour of oil comes from a substance dripping from a network of pipes. Thick coal dust carpets a section of concrete floor. Great iron walls hold in the licking flames of the large oil furnace. I slip on the pair of thick green glassed goggles over my eyes. The small steel door in the furnace wall opens and I look into the roasting flames. They blindingly dance up and down like bolts of lightning. My eyes almost burn amid the heat and flames of the furious inferno. Like something insane it seems to eat away the air. It fights and swirls and attacks at imagined foes. It jeers and laughs, shouting defiance at anyone trying to brave the flames and enter its domain. It tries to push and expand, but the small door shuts and the flames are imprisoned once again.

Boy, aged 11

The secret of the machines

We were taken from the ore-bed and the mine,
  We were melted in the furnace and the pit—
We were cast and wrought and hammered to design,
  We were cut and filed and tooled and gauged to fit.
Some water, coal, and oil is all we ask.
  And a thousandth of an inch to give us play:
And now, if you will set us to our task,
  We will serve you four and twenty hours a day!

  We can pull and haul and push and lift and drive,
  We can print and plough and weave and heat and light,
  We can run and race and swim and fly and dive,
  We can see and hear and count and read and write!

RUDYARD KIPLING

Clusters of electric bulbs
Like giant chrysanthemums
Paint the black cavern
With streaks and blots
Of faded yellow.
In grotesque mimicry
The monstrous shadows
Ape each movement of toiling men.
The stale pungent odour of unpacked earth
Tickles the nostrils.
Through the wood-plank roof
The dull-booming rumble
Of scampering traffic
Trickles in—
But is swallowed up
By the harsh purr of the drill
As it bites frenziedly
Into the dogged rock.

Overhead, unseen,
A mountain of stone is kept upright
By a slender steel beam
And a theory.

MAX ENDICOFF

The train

Out of the silence grows
An iron thunder—grows, and roars, and sweeps,
Menacing! The plain
Suddenly leaps,
Startled, from its repose—
Alert and listening. Now from the gloom
Of the soft distance loom
Three lights and, over them, a brush

Of tawny flame and flying spark—
Three pointed lights that rush,
Monstrous, upon the cringing dark.
And nearer, nearer rolls the sound,
Louder the throb and roar of wheels,
The shout of speed, the shriek of steam;
The sloping bank,

Cut into flashing squares, gives back the clank
And grind of metal, while the ground
Shudders and the bridge reels—
As, with a scream,
The train,

A rage of smoke, a laugh of fire,
A lighted anguish of desire,
A dream
Of gold and iron, of sound and flight,
Tumultuous roars across the night.

J. REDWOOD ANDERSON

The silence was uncanny. A faint scrambling sound behind them indicated that the other boys were making their way down the funnel and would at any moment be appearing like small white maggots. The silence in the cavern itself was so intense that the shaft of light from Alan's lamp seemed definitely to make a noise as it hit the walls with its circular blunted end, a flat ring about three feet in diameter. This medallion of light crept systematically over the roof of the cavern at the dictate of Alan's will directing his hand on the lamp. The sight was so fascinating that John still had not further examined the depth below, nor had he made any movement to get out of the mouth of the tunnel on to the ledge There he lay, on his stomach, with his head thrown back, staring upward at the explorations of the electric beam. Suddenly it movements stopped and both boys gazed awe-stricken at a vast cleft in the centre of the vault. It spread almost from one side to the other and then ended abruptly in a huge boss of rock which appeared to be hanging like a gigantic chandelier with nothing to support it. This pear-shaped rock glistened when the beam struck it, and the boys could see a trickle of moisture seeping through what appeared to be the sandy softness of its outer surface. From its lower lobe hung a huge stalk. It was a stalactite formed by the water that found its way from the upper earth down through the giant fissure and gathered round the rock before dripping through the cave with that faint clock-like tick-tock which John had heard when he first explored on the Sunday evening This gigantic needle shone flesh-coloured in the artificial light and the water trickling down gave the effect of a blood-stream within, or of the movement of muscles beneath the skin of a white human being.

from *The Cave* by RICHARD CHURCH

There's an interesting world
  under the ground.
A millipede sleeps, all curled
  like a ball.
    Keep quiet all
and let him sleep, safe and sound.
There's an interesting world
  under the ground.
You must not be heard
  for mice and lizards
  sleep through winter blizzards
until the spring comes round.
There's an interesting world
  under the ground.
Beetles, crickets and ladybirds
  a wasp so cunning
  sees a beetle running
the wasp flies down and the beetle dies.
There's an interesting world
  under the ground.
Mosses and lichens, in a crowd
  green and brown
  small and round
growing in a dusty cloud.
They're always on the move
  flying, burrowing and running
Bees flying into their hive
Worms eating leaves they've found
  They all live underground.
Underground's a wonderful place.

S. FREEMAN, aged 9

Under the sea

It is a fabulous place; when the tide is in, a wave-churned basin, creamy with foam, whipped by the combers that roll in from the whistling buoy on the reef. But when the tide goes out the little water world becomes quiet and lovely. The sea is very clear and the bottom becomes fantastic with hurrying, fighting, breeding animals. Crabs rush from frond to frond of the waving algae. Starfish squat over mussels and limpets, attach their million little suckers and then slowly lift with incredible power until the prey is broken from the rock. And then the starfish stomach comes out and envelops its food. Orange and speckled and fluted nudibrachs slide gracefully over the rocks, their skirts waving like the dresses of Spanish dancers. And black eels poke their heads out of crevices and wait for prey. The snapping shrimps with their trigger claws pop loudly. The lovely, coloured world is glassed over. Hermit crabs like frantic children scamper on the bottom sand. And now one, finding an empty snail shell he likes better than his own, creeps out, exposing his soft body to the enemy for a moment, and then pops into the new shell. A wave breaks over the barrier, and churns the glassy water for a moment and mixes bubbles into the pool, and then it clears and is tranquil and lovely and murderous again. Here a crab tears a leg from his brother. The anemones expand like soft and brilliant flowers, inviting any tired and perplexed animal to lie for a moment in their arms and when some small crab or little tide-pool Johnnie accepts the green and purple invitation, the petals whip in, the stinging cells shoot tiny narcotic needles into the prey, and it grows weak and perhaps sleepy while the searing caustic digestive acids melt its body down.

from *Cannery Row* by JOHN STEINBECK

Oyster shell

The oyster in his oyster shell,
In the sea, limitless,
Alone, in danger, confined,
His thoughts so sad.

Blind and artless,
He sleeps in rock shade,
But when he wakes he feels
The ebb and flow of tides.

At morning tide, at black dawn—
However bathed in light, in clearness—
The oyster's body, which must shrivel,
Stays locked in its shell.

The evening star, however clear
Its light, flashing on crests of waves,
May seem like the image of a dove
In a far field. But not to him.

Yes, it is sad. The wonder
Of the deep burden of the ocean
Night and day, unbearable:
In affliction, he shuts his shell.

Yet once the storm blows up,
On the day when sea-forests are uprooted,
The oyster's body which must shrivel,
How can it not be smashed?

KAMBARA YŪMEI

Crabs

Crabs, hiders in rock pools,
Scuttling out sideways when nobody's looking,
Ready to pinch an unwary toe.
How do you manage to disappear so completely
Down into the sand with such incredible speed?
If I manage to catch you
Your small beady eyes seem to look up to heaven,
Imploring to be saved from the fishmonger's slab.
All right, do not worry.
I shall let you go,
If only to see your amazing sideways exit.

KATHERINE TYRRELL

Old deep sing-song

in the old deep sing-song of the sea
in the old going-on of that sing-song
in that old mama-mama-mama going-on
of that nightlong daylong sleepsong
we look on   we listen
we lay by and hear
too many big bells   too many long gongs
too many weepers over a lost gone gold
too many laughs over light green gold
woven and changing in the wash and the heave
moving on the bottoms   winding in the waters
sending themselves with arms and voices
up in the old mama-mama-mama music
up into the whirl of spokes of light.

from *Wind Song* by CARL SANDBURG

The sea

Slapping of waves on a rocky shore.
White spray flying, as foam horses ride the waves,
Swirling around above, gulls hover,
Endlessly crying the same old cry,
A cry that never changes.

Clear water, bluey-greeny shades,
Lulling of the waves on a sunny day,
Floating of the ships at harbour side,
But still the endless cry of gulls.

Crunching of pebble on a beach.
Splash splash, as waves slap the pebbles.
Thundering sounds as pebbles crash
On to the beach.
Round and smooth and hot,
As the sun shines on all day.

LESLEY, aged 11

Boys

While kites eclipse the sun
And fly with the wind,
And boys haul on strings,
Keeping their toes entrenched in the sand,
Men, under the roofs of palm branches,
Peruse the sea.

Boys splash in the surf,
Crashing their fists against the waves—
Black fishes falling under thrashing gates of water
And coming up shaking,
While men pass nets across their knees
And look for holes.

Boys kick a ball on a hard, damp beach
And shout with screams of joy—
Pass me the ball nah man,
Pass me the ball—
While men carry cane on their shoulders
And their cutlasses shine.

Boys on bamboo rafts beyond the surf
Row along the bay,
And their friends turn somersaults through the foam
And swim towards them,
While men in gardens on the cliffside
Dig for yams.

Boys throw wood to the tops of trees
And with long sticks poke towards the heart
While green nuts fall like dead men,
And roll, and stop in silence—
While men whistle tunes and walk home
From the gardens.

CHRIS SEARLE, *Tobago*, 1969

Bright waves splash up from the rocks to refresh us,
blue sea-shells shift in their wake
and *there* is the thatch of the fishermen's houses, the path
made of pebbles, and look!
Small urchins combing the beaches
look up from their traps to salute us:

they remember us just as we left them.
The fisherman, hawking the surf on this side
of the reef, stands up in his boat
and hallos us: a starfish lies in its pool.
And gulls, white sails slanted seaward,
fly into the limitless morning before us.

from *Rights of Passage* by EDWARD BRATHWAITE

Smoke was rising here and there among the creepers that festooned the dead or dying trees. As they watched, a flash of fire appeared at the root of one wisp, and then the smoke thickened. Small flames stirred at the bole of a tree and crawled away through the leaves and brushwood, dividing and increasing. One patch touched a tree trunk and scrambled up like a bright squirrel. The smoke increased, sifted, rolled outwards. The squirrel leapt on the wings of the wind and clung to another standing tree, eating downwards. Beneath the dark canopy of leaves and smoke the fire laid hold on the forest and began to gnaw. Acres of black and yellow smoke rolled steadily towards the sea. At the sight of the flames and the irresistible course of the fire, the boys broke into shrill, excited cheering. The flames, as though they were a kind of wild life, crept as a jaguar creeps on its belly towards a line of birch-like saplings that fledged an outcrop of the pink rock. They flapped at the first of the trees, and the branches grew a brief foliage of fire. The heart of the flame leapt nimbly across the gap between the trees and then went swinging and flaring along the whole row of them. Beneath the capering boys a quarter of a mile square of forest was savage with smoke and flame. The separate noises of the fire merged into a drum-roll that seemed to shake the mountain.

from *Lord of the Flies* by WILLIAM GOLDING

As you enter the forest, your eyes get used to the glare of the sun, it seems dark and shadowy, and as cool as a butter-dish. The light is filtered through a million leaves, and so has a curious green aquarium-like quality which makes everything seem unreal. The centuries of dead leaves, that have fluttered to the ground have provided a rich layer of mould, soft as any carpet, and giving off a pleasant earthy smell. On every side are the huge trees, straddling on their great curling buttress roots, their great smooth trunks towering hundreds of feet above, their head foliage and branches merged indistinguishably into the endless green roof of the forest. Between these the floor of the forest is covered with the young trees, thin tender growths just shaken free of the cradle of leaf mould, long thin stalks with a handful of pale green leaves on top. They stand in the everlasting shade of their parents ready for the great effort of shooting up to the life-giving sun. In between their thin trunks, rambling across the floor of the forest one can see faint paths twisting and turning. These are the roads of the bush, and are followed by all its inhabitants.

There is no life to be seen in the great forest, except by chance, unless you know exactly where to look for it.

from *The Overloaded Ark* by GERALD DURRELL

Late summer

The pumpkin tendrils creep
Along the station platform.
A ladybird peeps
From a chink in the half-closed flowers.

A stopping train comes in.
No one gets on, or off.

On the millet stalk
Growing by the railing
The young ticket-man
Rests his clippers.

KINOSHITA YŪJI

Abundant snow

The silent, cold abundant snow
Chaps the explorer's fingers,
Weakening him on his journey.

The hard crinkling ice clubs together
In ridges everywhere.
The wind sweeps across the snow
Whistling and picking up snow
    as it blows along.

With numb fingers he sets up a camera
And takes shots of the silent world.
He crawls back into the tent with his friends.

He zips up his sleeping bag
And putting a few more blankets around him
He shuts his eyes to the world outside.

                  STEPHANIE ALLISS, aged 10

Icebergs

All night long a bright lookout was kept from every part of the deck; and whenever ice was seen on the one bow or the other, the helm was shifted and the yards braced, and, by quick working of the ship, she was kept clear. The accustomed cry of "Ice ahead!" "Ice on the lee bow!" "Another island!" in the same tones, and with the same orders following them, seemed to bring us directly back to our old position of the week before . . .

With a fair wind we soon ran clear of the field-ice, and by noon had only the stray islands floating far and near upon the ocean. The sun was out bright, the sea of a deep blue, fringed with the white foam of the waves, which ran high before a strong south-wester; our solitary ship tore on through the open water as though glad to be out of her confinement; and the ice islands lay scattered here and there, of various sizes and shapes, reflecting the bright rays of the sun, and drifting slowly northward before the gale. It was a contrast to much that we had lately seen, and a spectacle not only of beauty, but of life; for it required but little fancy to imagine these islands to be animate masses which had broken loose from the "thrilling regions of thick-ribbed ice," and were working their way, by wind and current, some alone, and some in fleets, to milder climes.

No pencil has ever yet given anything like the true effect of an iceberg. In a picture, they are huge, uncouth masses, stuck in the sea, while their chief beauty and grandeur—their slow, stately motion, the whirling of the snow about their summits, and the fearful groaning and cracking of their parts—the picture cannot give. This is the large iceberg, while the small and distant islands, floating on the smooth sea, in the light of a clear day, look like floating fairy isles of sapphire.

from *Two Years Before the Mast* by RICHARD DANA

Islands

The isle is full of noises,
Sounds, and sweet airs, that give delight, and hurt not.
Sometimes a thousand twangling instruments
Will hum about mine ears; and sometimes voices,
That, if I then had wak'd after long sleep,
Will make me sleep again; and then, in dreaming,
The clouds methought would open and show riches
Ready to drop upon me; that, when I wak'd,
I cried to dream again.

from *The Tempest* by WILLIAM SHAKESPEARE

I saw a thousand fearful wrecks,
A thousand men that fishes gnaw'd upon,
Wedges of gold, great ingots, heaps of pearl,
Inestimable stones, unvalu'd jewels,
All scatter'd in the bottom of the sea.
Some lay in dead men's skulls; and in those holes,
Where eyes did once inhabit, there were crept,
As 'twere in scorn of eyes, reflecting gems,
That woo'd the slimy bottom of the deep
And mock'd the dead bones that lay scatter'd by.

from *Richard III* by WILLIAM SHAKESPEARE

In the strange isle

In the strange isle,
In the green freckled wood and grassy glade,
Strangely the man, the panther and the shadow
Move by the well and the white stones.

Voices cry out in trees, and fingers beckon,
The wings of a million butterflies are sunlit eyes,
There is no sword
In the enchanted wood.

Branches bend over like a terror,
The sun is darkened,
The white wind and the sun and the curling wave
Cradle the coral shore and the tall forest.

Ceaseless the struggle in the twining circles,
The gulls, the doves, and the dark crows;
The fangs of the lily bleed, and the lips
Of the rose are torn.

Trees crash at midnight unpredicted,
Voices cry out,
Naked he walks, and with no fear,
In the strange isle, the wise and gentle.

MICHAEL ROBERTS

Island

The water lapping my memory
Calls back the boat pushing the green swell,
The creaking and straining of oars,
My uncle's dark voice and the smell of his tobacco.
We were coming at the island where for years
He said he would take me when the wind was right
Or when the island, so he said, was in the mood.
And so I knelt, trailing my hand in the water,
Listening to the sounds we made,
Wondering what was the island's mystery
Since no one lived there, or no one we knew about;
So he would say and wink, hinting something strange.

A solitary gull cut out its flight above us fast
As we pulled in on the crackling pebbles;
I would have looked about but must first heave in with him,
Or seem to help for I could have added little to the pull
Those knotted arms of his exerted on the rope.
I stumbled after in the wake of his enormous seaboots,
Floundering in the shingle, gulping in excitement
Of our exploration. Uninhabited—the word had charmed us
    both.
The rocks looked sharper, the air clearer, the breeze more salt.
Something sure to happen I might have told him,
Had I dared to use a word and risk the thought.

Climbing, hands hot with sweat, we clambered the immensity of
  rock
That backed the cove. I could hear him, breathing rough
Behind me, the sense of those coarse hands should I fall.
Then turf for our hands, after the harshness of the bare rock.
Across the top the wind scudded as I ran.
Now free, rolling over, leaping down the bank to the clump
Where I lay and looked over at the deeper green shapes of sea.
Breakers smashing the rocks, white gouts of foam.
I could have stayed forever, but we must go, down the broken
  cliff to the beach
To search for what the sea had left there, something up from the
  dark.
Past the line of stone he hurried by, nor would talk about;
Somebody lived there once, or died, he said—
Less said the better—as my skin tightened on my neck.
And soon we were back in the boat again pulling away from the
  island,
The line of stone-wall receding into the shapes of the rock
Leaving me to listen to the water, and the oars,
With the memory of that island somewhere.

PADDY KINSALE

Nothing can describe the confusion of thought which I felt when I sank into the water; for though I swam very well, yet I could not deliver myself from the waves so as to draw breath, till that wave having driven me, or rather carried me a vast way on towards the shore, and having spent itself, went back, and left me upon the land almost dry, but half-dead with the water I took in. I had so much presence of mind as well as breath left, that seeing myself nearer the mainland than I expected, I got upon my feet, and endeavoured to make on towards the land as fast as I could, before another wave should return, and take me up again. But I soon found it was impossible to avoid it; for I saw the sea come after me as high as a great hill, and as furious as an enemy which I had no means or strength to contend with; my business was to hold my breath, and raise myself upon the water, if I could; and so by swimming to preserve my breathing, and pilot myself towards the shore, if possible; my greatest concern now being, that the sea, as it would carry me a great way towards the shore when it came on, might not carry me back again with it when it gave back towards the sea.

The wave that came upon me again, buried me at once twenty or thirty foot deep in its own body; and I could feel myself carried with a mighty force and swiftness towards the shore a very great way; but I held my breath, and assisted my self to swim still forward with all my might. I was ready to burst with holding my breath, when, as I felt myself rising up, so to my immediate relief, I found my head and hands shoot out above the surface of the water; and though it was not two seconds of time that I could keep myself so, yet it relieved me greatly, gave me breath and new courage. I was covered again with water a good while, but not so long but I held it out; and finding the water had spent itself, and began to return, I struck forward against the return of the waves, and felt ground again with my feet. I stood still a few

moments to recover breath, and till the water went from me, and
then took to my heels, and ran with what strength I had farther
towards the shore. But neither would this deliver me from the
fury of the sea, which came pouring in after me again, and twice
more I was lifted up by the waves and carried forwards as before,
the shore being very flat.

The last time of these two had well near been fatal to me; for
the sea having hurried me along as before, landed me, or rather
dashed me against a piece of a rock, and that with such force as
it left me senseless, and indeed helpless as to my own deliverance;
for the blow taking my side and breast, beat the breath as it were
quite out of my body; and had it returned again immediately, I
must have been strangled in the water; but I recovered a little
before the return of the waves, and seeing I should be covered
again with the water, I resolved to hold fast by a piece of the rock,
and so to hold my breath, if possible, till the wave went back;
now as the waves were not so high as at first, being nearer land,
I held my hold till the wave abated, and then fetched another run,
which brought me so near the shore, that the next wave, though
it went over me, yet did not so swallow me up as to carry me
away, and the next run I took, I got to the mainland, where, to
my great comfort, I clambered up the cliffs of the shore and sat
me down upon the grass, free from danger, and quite out of the
reach of the water . . .

I walked about on the shore, lifting up my hands, and my
whole being, as I may say, wrapped up in the contemplation of
my deliverance, making a thousand gestures and motions which
I cannot describe, reflecting upon all my comrades that were
drowned, and that there should not be one soul saved but myself;
for, as for them, I never saw them afterwards, or any sign of them,
except three of their hats, one cap, and two shoes that were not
fellows . . .

After I had solaced my mind with the comfortable part of my condition, I began to look round me to see what kind of place I was in, and what next to be done, and I soon found my comforts abate, and that in a word I had a dreadful deliverance: for I was wet, had no clothes to shift me, not any thing either to eat or drink to comfort me, neither did I see any prospect before me, but that of perishing with hunger, or being devoured by wild beasts; and that which was particularly afflicting to me was that I had no weapon either to hunt and kill any creature for my sustenance, or to defend myself against any other creature that might desire to kill me for theirs. In a word, I had nothing about me but a knife, a tobacco-pipe, and a little tobacco in a box; this was all my provision, and this threw me into terrible agonies of mind, that for a while I ran about like a madman. Night coming upon me, I began with a heavy heart to consider what would be my lot if there were any ravenous beasts in that country, seeing at night they always come abroad for their prey.

All the remedy that offered to my thoughts at that time was to get up into a thick bushy tree like a fir, but thorny, which grew near me, and where I resolved to sit all night, and consider the next day what death I should die, for as yet I saw no prospect of life; I walked about a furlong from the shore, to see if I could find any fresh water to drink, which I did, to my great joy; and having drunk and put a little tobacco in my mouth to prevent hunger, I went to the tree, and getting up into it, endeavoured to place myself so, as that if I should sleep I might not fall; and having cut me a short stick, like a truncheon, for my defence, I took up my lodging, and having been excessively fatigued, I fell fast asleep and slept as comfortably as, I believe, few could have done in my condition, and found myself the most refreshed with it that I think I ever was on such an occasion.

from *Robinson Crusoe* by DANIEL DEFOE

Relic

I found this jawbone at the sea's edge:
There, crabs, dogfish, broken by the breakers or tossed
To flap for half an hour and turn to a crust
Continue the beginning. The deeps are cold:
In that darkness camaraderie does not hold:
Nothing touches but, clutching, devours. And the jaws,
Before they are satisfied or their stretched purpose
Slacken, go down jaws; go gnawn bare. Jaws
Eat and are finished and the jawbone comes to the beach:
This is the sea's achievement; with shells,
Vertibrae, claws, carapaces, skulls.

Time in the sea eats its tail, thrives, casts these
Indigestibles, the spars of purposes
That failed far from the surface. None grow rich
In the sea. This curved jawbone did not laugh
But gripped, gripped and is now a cenotaph.

TED HUGHES

Ruins and remains

The dismantled ship

In some unused lagoon, some nameless bay,
On sluggish, lonesome waters, anchor'd near the shore,
An old, dismasted, gray and batter'd ship, disabled, done,
After free voyages to all the seas of earth, haul'd up at last and
    hawser'd tight
Lies rusting, mouldering.

WALT WHITMAN

The gasworks

The smell like rotten eggs,
The noises—hiss clang, erc, clink,
The machines, turning, moving,
Chains turning, moving the axle,
Hissss goes the steam.

Boilers building up pressure,
Heat, searing, blinding heat,
The conveyors moving, clanking, clupping;
CRASH goes the coal onto another conveyor,
BUFF as the coal trucks hit each other,
HOOOEEEE as the trains go past.
Diesels, locos.

Cooling towers, the water drip drip dripping down,
Unused turntables bumping underfoot,
Buncock and Wilcox boilers, coal-fired,
Chain stoker feed,
Cogs and wheels,
Drums and barrels.
Pipes: bending pipes, straight pipes, thin pipes,
Hissing pipes, steaming pipes, thick pipes.

Dust, grime smell smoke,
Stairs, iron, steel,
Rust corroding the pipes,
Stairs, boilers and machines,
Gear boxes, regulators, registers, thermometers.

TERRY, aged 12

The ruin

Wonderful is this wall of stone, wrecked by fate.
The city buildings crumble, the bold works of the giants decay.
Roofs have caved in, towers collapsed,
Barred gates are gone, gateways have gaping mouths, hoar frost
   clings to mortar.
Ceilings save nothing from the fury of storms, worn away,
   tottering,
Undermined by age. The earth's embrace,
Its clammy grip, has claimed the mighty craftsmen;
They are perished, gone. A hundred generations of men
Have passed away since then. This wall, grey with lichen
And red of hue, outlives kingdom after kingdom,
Weathers wild storms; the tall gate succumbed
But the wall itself still stands, hacked at by weapons . . .

. . . .

The architect conceived a remarkable plan:
Ingenious and resolute, he bound the foundations
With metal rods into linking rings.
The city walls were beautiful, the bath-houses plentiful,
A wealth of gables stood in the sky; thunderous was the martial
   clamour;
All the many mead-halls overflowed with merriment.
But fate, inexorable, swept all this away.
Slaughtered men fell far and wide, plague tortured the town,
Death struck down every valiant man.
Their deserted ramparts became waste places,
The derelict city decayed. Its warriors and craftsmen
Lay dead in the earth. Thus these lordly courts are crumbling;
Over the redstone arch the roof framework

Is a skeleton, untiled. The ruins have tumbled to the plain
Broken into craggy mounds of stone. Here, long ago, many a
   happy man
Was clothed resplendently in glowing gold.
Proud and flushed with wine, in his shining armour
He gazed upon his treasure . . . silver and curious stones,
Gold, gems, and precious jewels . . .
And he gazed at this fine castle, too, built in a great kingdom.
Stone houses stood here, and a hot spring
Gushed from the earth in a swift stream.
The stone wall encompassed all,
The gaily painted baths ceaselessly supplied with steaming
   water.
The scalding water streams across the grey stones
Into the circular pool where the baths were . . .

. . . .

That city was a noble place.   ·

Translated from the Anglo-Saxon by KEVIN CROSSLEY-HOLLAND

Angkor Wat,
Cambodia

Suburbs

The drizzle slants down over the grey suburbs.
It always drizzles over the suburbs, in time with
the windscreen wipers and the houses.
Up go my eyes over the gables, down to gutters, up, down,
up, down with a monotony broken only at the
regular junctions with dismal tributary roads.
Each house a blotched and bleary face, with
beady, deepset vicious little window eyes and
blistered, beery noses.
Each house the same, each face more gruesomely
distorted than the last.

The curveless 'crescents' one-sided 'squares'
and treeless 'avenues' are all shelves.
They are the shelves in a laboratory to hold
the bottles that are never used.
Over the years of decay the contents of these
dusty terraces of bottles have gone bad and have
begun to smell.
The shelves are getting woodworm; one day they
will collapse.
The bottles will fall and break and let out the
revengeful smells . . .

CHARLES MARTIN, aged 12

The dull dusty road is outlined by old tatty houses.
The broken windows are scattered on the path.
Through the windows you can see old flowered wallpaper and
    dirty curtains.
The favourite colour seems to be yellow.
The tops of the houses lean over,
They nearly meet in the middle of the dirty road.
Through the cracks in the paving-stones weeds are growing.
The old road has great big cracks in it.
The top halves of the houses were white but
Now they are grey.
Over the grey paint are dark pieces of wood,
Part of the wood has come off.
Now nobody lives in the houses but some of them
Have chairs, tables and sideboards in the rooms.
If you look through the windows you can see the dusty floor-
    boards.
The windows have pictures of people made of lines on them.
People have started to write on the doors of the old houses.
The bricks are beginning to break.
Further along the road the houses have started to be pulled down.
Soon the houses are going to be pulled down too.

ROSEMARY BROMLEY, aged 10

The deserted house

There's no smoke in the chimney,
And the rain beats on the floor;
There's no glass in the window,
There's no wood in the door;
The heather grows behind the house,
And the sand lies before.

No hand hath trained the ivy,
The walls are grey and bare;
The boats upon the sea sail by,
Nor ever tarry there.
No beast of the field comes nigh,
Nor any bird of the air.

MARY COLERIDGE

I am . . .
Down by the station, the old railroad station,
Where the floors are coloured with ground-in dust;
The benches moan with tired, brief creaks,
Their metal legs eaten by rust.

Outside . . .
The dirt-brown stairs bake in the sun;
The paint on the walls is peeling.
Four rows of track gleam . . . and smell
Metallic and fresh—yet worn.

And . . .
You can see the heat as it patterns the air,
The blue of the sky softly rests on the roof.
All this to see, and no one to see it;
There's no one—no one but me.

Wondering . . .
The cars without the drivers,
The benches without their occupants,
Wondering at the empty loneliness of the place,
Which somehow might be filled.

JOHN RATHE, aged 12

The fire

As I looked at the old mill I wondered what it would be like if I were that mill, sitting in solitude without sympathy. How lonely that old, burnt-out mill must be, wrapped in deathly silence with the crumbled mass of stone and wood and twisted and slashed metalwork.

As you look the cold, fevery sound of creaking timber is shattering the horrible silence which covers the loud noise of the cars and lorries passing in the distance. Oh how I hate to see the dead skeleton of a ghostly place hoping for renewal.

As you look at it you wish you were far, far away. The straggling girders are now lying around like meat of a dead animal after being attacked by a lit-up enemy. As you look at it, it looks like a whole lot of rocking horses. Then you see charred wood strewn all around.

The deathly silence is suddenly torpedoed by chirping and twittering birds which are still wondering how it all happened. Their nests gutted like the old mill itself. How terrible it must be to have no home.

All the chippings are all over the ground with long and terribly crooked beams. As I look the birds are looking too at their roasted eggs lying terribly scarred and smashed after the fiery flames of death.

BOY, aged 11

The old tree

The old oak tree,
hangs decayed branches which are
bending and twisting.
The old tree has bent itself over
Like a person with a bent back.

No bird sits on this leafless tree,
No bird sings for this lonely tree.
This weather beated tree stands in
a desolate garden.

This tree is small,
there is a small hole
at the bottom of this tree
and ants crawl under.
This desolate tree just waits.

HELEN, aged 11

A withered tree

Not a twig or a leaf on the old tree,
Wind and frost harm it no more.
A man could pass through the hole in its belly,
Ants crawl searching under its peeling bark.
Its only lodger, the toadstool which dies in a morning,
The birds no longer visit in the twilight.
But its wood can still spark tinder.
It does not care yet to be only the void at its heart.

HAN YU

The old fire engine

Where I liked it best, though, was on the other side of the park where the old fire engine was.

You had to crawl through like a big drain pipe at the edge of the park, it was an old sewer, I think, and where it brought you out was in a long road with houses that had been there for ages, made out of stone. You were clean out of the estate then. You just had to walk up this road and there was a coal-mine there with a lot of slag heaps, and railway lines that went right over the street, so that lorries bumped when they went over them. The houses were all in long rows and made of black stone, and all the streets were just rough cobbles with sooty grass growing through them. Not like *our* blinking street . . .

We used to go on these slag heaps, getting old pram wheels that people had thrown away, and playing on this big second-hand fire engine that they had, standing on a patch of old concrete nearby . . .

There was nothing like this fire engine on *our* estate. It was a big Leyland. All the ladders and bells and that had been stripped off but there was still like that platform where the firemen used to sit. It had done 45 000 miles. It had been painted navy blue, but you could still tell it was a fire engine. I think they used to use it for lugging stuff up on to the slag heaps, but it had stood on this patch of concrete as long as *I* can remember. We used to play at fire engines on it. The fellow who used to mind the slag heaps, he didn't mind you playing on it, but if the railway police came up and found you on it, they used to take your name and address.

from *There is a Happy Land* by KEITH WATERHOUSE

Reflections

On the moors it is very quiet,
On your own.
There's nobody around
Except yourself.
It's peaceful there
When you stop and think.
Stone walls at the back of you,
Maybe a few donkeys on the moor.
There's no more noise of the war
For you to listen for,
No more screaming, no more shouting
Just peace and quiet.
No more blasting of the bombs
Just green grass for miles and miles.
All is dead,
Except yourself,
You're on the moors, alone
No friend with you:
This is real peace.

WENDY MAGGS, aged 11

Trout

Hangs, a fat gun-barrel,
deep under arched bridges
or slips like butter down
the throat of the river.

From depths smooth-skinned as plums
his muzzle gets bull's eye;
picks off grass-seed and moths
that vanish, torpedoed.

Where water unravels
over gravel-bed he
is fired from the shallows
white belly reporting

Creatures

flat; darts like a tracer-
bullet back between stones
and is never burnt out.
A volley of cold blood

ramrodding the current.

SEAMUS HEANEY

The rockfish

Flop. The cone-shaped bar of lead tied to the end of the fishing-line dropped into the sea without causing a ripple. It sank rapidly through the long seaweed that grew on the face of the rock. It sank twenty-five feet and then struck the bottom. It tumbled around and then lay on its side in a niche at the top of a round pool. The man on top of the rock hauled in his line until it was taut. The bar of lead bobbled up and down twice. Then it rested straight on its end in the niche. Three short plaits of stiff horsehair extended crookedly like tentacles from the line above the leaden weight at regular intervals. At the end of each plait was a hook baited all over with shelled periwinkle. A small crab, transfixed through the belly, wriggled on the lowest hook. The two upper hooks had a covering of crushed crab tied by thin strings around the periwinkles. The three baited hooks swung round and round, glistening white through the red strands of broad seaweed that hung lazily from their stems in the rock face. Dark caverns at the base of the rock cast long shadows out over the bottom of the sea about the hooks. Little bulbous things growing in groups on the bottom spluttered methodically as they stirred.

The man sitting above on the top of the rock spat into the sea. Resting his fishing-rod in the crutch of his right arm, he began to fill his pipe, yawning.

A little rockfish came rushing out from a cavern under the rock. He whisked his tail and stopped dead behind a huge blade of seaweed when he saw the glistening baits. His red scaly body was the colour of the weed. It tapered from the middle to the narrow tail and to the triangular-shaped head. He stared at the baits for a long time without moving his body. His gills rose and fell steadily. Then he flapped his tail and glided to the upper hook. He touched it with his snout. He nibbled at it timorously three times. Then he snatched at the top of it and darted away back into the cavern with a piece of periwinkle in his mouth. The man on the rock sat up excitedly, threw his pipe on the rock, and seized the rod with both hands, breathing through his nose.

Several rockfish gathered around the little fellow in the cavern. They tried to snatch the piece of periwinkle from his mouth. But he dived under a ledge of rock and bolted it hurriedly. Then, all the rockfish darted out to the hooks. The little ones scurried around hither and thither. Three middle-sized ones stood by the two upper hooks, sniffing at them. Then they began to nibble carefully. One little rockfish stood on his head over the bottom hook and sniffed at it. But the crab wriggled one leg and the rockfish darted away at a terrific speed. All the rockfish darted away after it into the cavern. Then one of the middle-sized ones came back again alone. He went up to the highest hook and grabbed at it immediately. He took the whole bait from it. The hook grazed his lower lip as it slipped from his mouth. The rockfish dropped the bait, turned a somersault, and dived into the cavern.

The man on the rock swung his rod back over his head, and dropped it forward again with an oath when he found the line coming slack. 'Missed,' he said. Then the leaden weight slipped back again into the niche. A crowd of rockfish quarrelled over the pieces of periwinkle fallen from the middle-sized fellow's mouth. The pieces, too light to sink, kept floating about. Then they disappeared one by one into the fishes' mouths.

A huge rockfish prowled in from the deep. He stood by the corner of a rock watching the little ones quarrel over the pieces of fallen bait. He was as big as all the others together. He must have been three feet long and his middle was as thick as a bull-dog's chest. The scales on his back were all the colours of the rainbow. His belly was a dun colour. He stood still for a time, watching like an old bull, his gills showing large red cavities in his throat as they opened. Then he swooped in among the little ones. They dived away from him into the cavern. He gobbled the remaining pieces of bait. Then he turned around slowly twice and swam close to the bottom towards the hooks. He saw the crab wriggling on the lowest hook. With a rush he swallowed the crab and the hook, turned about and rushed away with it, out towards his lair in the deep. The leaden weight rushed along the bottom with him. The line went taut with a snap over his back. The fishing-rod was almost wrenched from the hands of the man on the rock. Its tip touched the water. Then the man heaved the rod over his head and grasped the line. The hook was wrenched back out of the rockfish's gullet and its point tore through the side of his mouth.

The rockfish was whirled about by the wrench and dragged backwards headlong. With a swishing sound he heaved straight through the water towards the cavern. Then the line went taut again as the man hauled in. The rockfish was tugged up along the face of the rock. He jumped twice and heaved. He tore a strip of the soft thick skin in which the hook was embedded from his jaw at one end. Hanging to the hook by this strip, he came up gasping through the hanging weeds. The man groaned as he heaved.

Then the bared top hook got caught in a broad blade of sea-weed. It combed its way through to the hard stem and then got stuck. The man heaved and could draw it no farther. The rockfish hung exhausted from the bottom of the hook. The man stuck his right foot against a ledge and leaning back with the line held in his two hands across his stomach he pulled with all his might. The top hook broke. The line jerked up. The rockfish reached the surface. He tried to breathe with wide open mouth. Then he hurled himself into the air and dived headlong downwards. The hanging strip of skin parted from his jaw. He was free.

LIAM O'FLAHERTY

Lemmings

Lemmings die every year. Over the cliff
They pour, hot blood into cold sea
So that you half imagine steam
Will rise. They do not part company
At first, but spread out, a brown team
Like seaweed, undulant and tough.

Light changes and the wind may veer
As they swim out and on. The sea
May become sleek or shrewish. Foam
May blind them or may let them see
The wet horizon. It takes time.
They do not die within an hour.

One by one they leave the air
And drown as individuals.
From minute to minute they blink out
Like aeroplanes or stars or gulls
Whose vanishing is never caught.
All in time will disappear.

from *Just Like the Resurrection* by PATRICIA BEER

Adolf

When we were children our father often worked on the night-shift. Once it was spring-time, and he used to arrive home, black and tired, just as we were downstairs in our nightdresses. Then night met morning face to face, and the contact was not always happy. Perhaps it was painful to my father to see us gaily entering upon the day into which he dragged himself soiled and weary. He didn't like going to bed in the spring morning sunshine.

But sometimes he was happy, because of his long walk through the dewy fields in the first daybreak. He loved the open morning, the crystal and the space, after a night down pit. He watched every bird, every stir in the trembling grass, answered the whinnying of the peewits and tweeted to the wrens. If he could, he also would have whinnied and tweeted and whistled in a native language that wasn't human. He liked non-human things best.

One sunny morning we were all sitting at table when we heard his heavy slurring walk up the entry. We became uneasy. His was always a disturbing presence, trammeling. He passed the window darkly, and we heard him go into the scullery and put down his tin bottle. But directly he came into the kitchen we felt at once that he had something to communicate. No one spoke.

We watched his black face for a second.

'Give me a drink,' he said.

My mother hastily poured out his tea. He went to pour it out into his saucer. But instead of drinking it he suddenly put something on the table among the tea-cups. A tiny brown rabbit! A small rabbit, a mere morsel, sitting against the bread as still as if it were a made thing.

'A rabbit! A young one! Who gave it you, Father?'

But he laughed, enigmatically, with a sliding motion of his yellow-gray eyes, and went to take off his coat. We pounced on the rabbit.

'Is it alive? Can you feel its heart beat?'

My father came back and sat down heavily in his armchair. He dragged his saucer to him, and blew his tea, pushing out his red lips under his black moustache.

'Where did you get it, Father?'

'I picked it up,' he said, wiping his fore-arm over his mouth and beard.

'Where?'

'It's a wild one!' came my mother's quick voice.

'Yes, it is.'

'Then why did you bring it?' cried my mother.

'Oh, we wanted it,' came our cry.

'Yes, I've no doubt you did,' retorted my mother. But she was drowned in our clamour of questions. On the field-path my father had found a dead mother rabbit and three dead little ones—this one alive, but unmoving.

'But what had killed them, Daddy?'

'I couldn't say, my child. I s'd think she'd aten something.'

'Why did you bring it!' again my mother's voice of condemnation. 'You know what it will be.'

My father made no answer, but we were loud in protest.

'He must bring it. It's not big enough to live by itself.'

'It would die,' we shouted.

'Yes, and it will die now. And then there'll be another outcry.'

My mother set her face against the tragedy of dead pets. Our hearts sank.

'It won't die, Father, will it? Why will it? It won't.'

'I s'd think not,' said my father.

'You know well enough it will. Haven't we had it all before!' said my mother.

'They dunna always pine,' replied my father testily.

But my mother reminded him of other little wild animals he had brought, which had sulked and refused to live, and brought storms of tears and trouble in our house of lunatics. Trouble fell on us. The little rabbit sat on our lap, unmoving, its eyes wide and dark. We brought it milk, warm milk, and held it to its nose. It sat as still as if it was far away, retreated down some deep burrow, hidden, oblivious. We wetted its mouth and whiskers with drops of milk. It gave no sign, did not even shake off the wet, white drops. Somebody began to shed a few secret tears.

'What did I say?' cried my mother. 'Take it and put it down in the field.'

Her command was in vain. We were driven to get dressed for school. There sat the rabbit. It was like a tiny obscure cloud. Watching it, the emotions died out of our breast. Unless to love it, to yearn over it. Its feelings were all ambushed. They must be circumvented. Love and affection were a trespass upon it. A little wild thing, it became more mute and asphyxiated still in its own arrest, when we approached with love. We must not love it. We must circumvent it, for its own existence.

So I passed the order to my sister and mother. The rabbit was not to be spoken to, or even looked at. Wrapping it in a piece of flannel, I put it in an obscure corner of the cold parlour, and put a saucer of milk before its nose. My mother was forbidden to enter the parlour while we were at school.

'As if I should take any notice of your nonsense,' she cried, affronted. Yet I doubt if she ventured into the parlour.

At midday, after school, creeping into the front room, there we saw the rabbit still and unmoving in the piece of flannel. Strange grey-brown neutralisation of life, still living! It was a sore problem to us.

'Why won't it drink its milk, Mother?' we whispered. Our father was asleep.

'It prefers to sulk its life away, silly little thing.'

A profound problem. Prefers to sulk its life away!

We put young dandelion leaves to its nose. The sphinx was not more oblivious. Yet its eye was bright.

At teatime, however, it had hopped a few inches, out of its flannel, and there it sat again, uncovered, a little solid cloud of muteness, with unmoving whiskers. Only its side palpitated slightly with life.

Darkness came. My father set out for work. The rabbit was still unmoving. Dumb despair was coming over the sisters, a threat of tears before bedtime. Clouds of my mother's anger gathered as she muttered against my father's wantonness.

Once more the rabbit was wrapped in the old pit-singlet. But now it was carried into the scullery and put under the copper fire-place, that it might imagine itself inside a burrow. The saucers were placed about, four or five, here and there on the floor, so that if the little creature should chance to hop abroad, it could not fail to come upon some food. After this my mother was allowed to take from the scullery what she wanted and then she was forbidden to open the door.

When morning came and it was light, I went downstairs. Opening the scullery door, I heard a slight scuffle. Then I saw dabbles of milk all over the floor and tiny rabbit-droppings in the saucers. And there was the miscreant, the tips of his ears showing behind a pair of boots. I peeped at him. He sat bright-eyed and askance, twitching his nose and looking at me while not looking at me.

He was alive—very much alive. But we were still afraid to trespass on his confidence.

'Father!' My father was arrested at the door. 'Father, the rabbit's alive!'

'Back you life it is,' said my father.

'Mind how you go in.'

By evening, however, the little creature was tame, quite tame. He was christened Adolf. We were enchanted by him. We couldn't really love him, because he was wild and loveless to the end. But he was an unmixed delight.

We decided he was too small to live in a hutch—he must live at large in the house. My mother protested, but in vain. He was so tiny. So we had him upstairs, and he dropped tiny pills on the bed and we were enchanted.

Adolf made himself instantly at home. He had the run of the house and was perfectly happy, with his tunnels and his holes behind the furniture.

We loved him to take meals with us. He would sit on the table humping his back, sipping his milk, shaking his whiskers and his tender ears, hopping off and hobbling back to his saucer, with an air of supreme unconcern. Suddenly he was alert. He hobbled a few tiny paces, and reared himself up inquisitively at the sugar-basin. He fluttered his tiny forepaws, and then reached and laid them on the edge of the basin, whilst he craned his thin neck and peeped in. He trembled his whiskers at the sugar, then did his best to lift down a lump.

'*Do* you think I will have it! Animals in the sugar-pot!' cried my mother with a rap of her hand on the table.

Which so delighted the electric Adolf that he flung his hind-quarters and knocked over a cup.

'It's your own fault, Mother. If you left him alone—'

He continued to take tea with us. He rather liked warm tea. And he loved sugar. Having nibbled a lump, he would turn to the butter. There he was shoo'd off by our parent. He soon learned to treat her shooing with indifference. Still, she hated him to put his nose in the food. And he loved to do it. And one day between them they overturned the cream-jug. Adolf deluged his little chest, bounced back in terror, was seized by his little ears by my mother and bounced down on the hearth-rug. There he shivered in momentary discomfort and suddenly set off in a wild flight to the parlour.

This last was his happy hunting-ground. He had cultivated the bad habit of pensively nibbling certain bits of cloth in the hearth-rug. When chased from this pasture, he would retreat under the sofa. There he would twinkle in meditation until suddenly, no one knew why, he would go off like an alarm clock. With a sudden bumping scuffle he would whirl out of the room, going through the doorway with his little ears flying. Then we would hear his thunderbolt hurtling in the parlour, but before we could follow, the wild streak of Adolf would flash past us, on an electric wind that swept him round the scullery and carried him back, a little mad thing, flying possessed like a ball round the parlour. After which ebullition he would sit in a corner composed and distant, twitching his whiskers in abstract meditation. And it was in vain we questioned him about his outbursts. He just went off like a gun, and was as calm after it as a gun that smokes placidly.

Alas! he grew up rapidly. It was almost impossible to keep him from the outer door.

One day, as we were playing by the stile, I saw his brown shadow loiter across the road and pass into the field that faced the houses. Instantly a cry of 'Adolf!'—a cry he knew full well. And instantly a wind swept him away down the sloping meadow, tail twinkling and zig-zagging through the grass. After him we pelted. It was a strange sight to see him, ears back, his little loins so powerful, flinging the world behind him. We ran ourselves out of breath, but we could not catch him. Then somebody headed him off, and he sat with sudden unconcern, twitching his nose under a bunch of nettles.

His wanderings cost him a shock. One Sunday morning my father had just been quarrelling with a pedlar, and we were hearing the aftermath indoors, when there came a sudden unearthly scream from the yard. We flew out; there sat Adolf cowering under a bench, whilst a great black-and-white cat glowered intently at him a few yards away. Sight not to be forgotten. Adolf rolling back his eyes and parting his strange muzzle in another scream, the cat stretching forward in slow elongation.

Ha! how we hated that cat! How we pursued him over the chapel wall and across the neighbours' gardens. Adolf was still only half-grown.

'Cats!' said my mother. 'Hideous detestable animals! Why do people harbour them?'

But Adolf was becoming too much for her. Suddenly to hear him clumping downstairs when she was alone in the house was startling. And to keep him from the door impossible. Cats prowled outside. It was worse than having a child to look after. Yet we would not have him shut up. He became more lusty, more callous than ever. He was a strong kicker, and many a scratch on face and arms did we owe to him. But he brought his own doom on himself. The lace curtains in the parlour—my mother was rather proud of them—fell on the floor very full. One of Adolf's joys was to scuffle wildly through them as though through some foamy undergrowth. He had already torn rents in them.

One day he entangled himself altogether. He kicked, he whirled round in a mad nebulous inferno. He screamed—and brought down the curtain-rod with a smash, right on the best beloved geranium just as my mother rushed in. She extricated him, but she never forgave him.

Even we understood that he must go. It was decided, after a long deliberation, that my father should carry him back to the wild woods. Once again he was stowed into the great pocket of the pit-jacket.

'Best pop him i' th' pot,' said my father, who enjoyed raising the wind of indignation.

And so, next day, our father said that Adolf, set down on the edge of the coppice, had hopped away with utmost indifference, neither elated nor moved. We heard it and believed. But many, many were the heart-searchings. How would the other rabbits receive him? Would they smell his tameness, his humanised degradation, and rend him? My mother pooh-poohed the extravagant idea.

However, he was gone, and we were rather relieved. My father kept an eye open for him. He declared that several times passing the coppice in the early morning, he had seen Adolf peeping through the nettle-stalks. He had called him in an odd, high-voiced, cajoling fashion. But Adolf had not responded. Wildness gains so soon upon its creatures. And they become so contemptuous then of our tame presence. So it seemed to me. I myself would go to the edge of the coppice, and call softly. I myself would imagine bright eyes between the nettle-stalks, flash of a white scornful tail past the bracken. That insolent white tail, as Adolf turned his flank on us.

from *Phoenix* by D. H. LAWRENCE

Snakes

A basketful of ritual cobras
comes into the tame little house,
their brown-wheat glisten ringed with ripples.
They lick the room with their bodies, curves
uncurling, writing a sibilant alphabet of panic
on my floor. Mother gives them milk
in saucers. She watches them suck
and bare the black-line design
etched on the brass of the saucer.
The snakeman wreathes their writhing
round his neck
for father's smiling
money. But I scream.

A. K. RAMANUJAN

Horses

Horses stand up still on the skyline,
Waiting for something to happen;
Strangely thoughtful with big sad eyes,
Watching the rain fall mistily,
The clouds move, or just the distance
Escaping from them.
Horses gallop sometimes—up hills,
Across fields, thundering wild,
In a mad explosion of power;
Hot, steaming, violently animal,
But specially, individually horse.
They flail the air and the ground,
Hard-stiff on legs bone-right
And solid-hooved of nail and iron.
They fetlock thrash the tufts of grass and hair,
Rioting down bone and sinew,
Hurrying to be there.
Gigantically gentle with children,
They feel friendly to the touch,
And take sugar quietly.
Stallion-proud and still they look back
To their primeval youth.
They have learned to be patient.

PADDY KINSALE

Death of a bird

After those first days
When we had placed him in his iron cage
And made a space for him
From such

Outrageous cage of wire,
Long and shallow, where the sunlight fell
Through the air, onto him;
After

He had been fed for three days
Suddenly, in that sunlight before noon
He was dead with no
Pretence.

He did not say goodbye,
He did not say thank you, but he died then
Lying flat on the rigid
Wires

Of his cage, his gold
Beak shut tight, which once in hunger had
Opened as a trap
And then

Swiftly closed again,
Swallowing quickly what I had given him;
How can I say I am sorry
He died.

Seeing him lie there dead,
Death's friend with death, I was angry he
 Had gone without pretext or warning
  With no

Suggestion first he should go,
Since I had fed him, then put wires round him,
 Bade him hop across
  The bars of my hands.

I asked him only that
He should desire his life. He had become
 Of us a black friend with
  A gold mouth

Shrilly singing through
The heat. The labour of the black bird! I
 Cannot understand why
  He is dead.

I bury him familiarly.
His heritage is a small brown garden.
Something is added to the everlasting earth;
From my mind a space is taken away.

JON SILKIN

Humming bird

I can imagine, in some other world
Primeval-dumb, far back
In that most awful stillness, that only gasped and hummed,
Humming-birds raced down the avenues.

Before anything had a soul,
While life was a heave of Matter, half inanimate,
This little bit chipped off in brilliance
And went whizzing through the slow, vast, succulent stems.

I believe there were no flowers then,
In the world where the humming-bird flashed ahead of creation.
I believe he pierced the slow vegetable veins with his long beak.

Probably he was big
As mosses, and little lizards, they say, were once big.
Probably he was a jabbing, terrifying monster.

We look at him through the wrong end of the long telescope of
   Time.

Luckily for us.

D. H. Lawrence

Print from a stone-cut by a contemporary Eskimo artist.

Gipsies

The gipsies seek wide sheltering woods again,
With droves of horses flock to mark their lane,
And trample on dead leaves, and hear the sound,
And look and see the black clouds gather round,
And set their camps, and free from muck and mire,
And gather stolen sticks to make the fire.
The roasted hedgehog, bitter though as gall,
Is eaten up and relished by them all.
They know the woods and every fox's den
And get their living far away from men;
The shooters ask them where to find the game,
The rabbits know them and are almost tame.
The aged women, tawny with the smoke,
Go with the winds and crack the rotted oak.

JOHN CLARE

Ancestors

1 Every Friday morning my grandfather
left his farm of canefields, chickens, cows,
and rattled in his trap down to the harbour town
to sell his meat. He was a butcher.
Six-foot-three and very neat: high collar,
winged, a grey cravat, a waistcoat, watch-
chain just above the belt, thin narrow-
bottomed trousers, and the shoes his wife
would polish every night. He drove the trap
himself: slap of the leather reins
along the horse's back and he'd be off
with a top-hearted homburg on his head:
black English country gentleman.

Now he is dead. The meat shop burned,
his property divided. A doctor bought
the horse. His mad alsatians killed it.
The wooden trap was chipped and chopped
by friends and neighbours and used to stop-
gap fences and for firewood. One yellow
wheel was rolled across the former cowpen gate.
Only his hat is left. I 'borrowed' it.
I used to try it on and hear the night wind
man go battering through the canes, cocks waking up and
    thinking
it was dawn throughout the clinking country night.
Great caterpillar tractors clatter down
the broken highway now; a diesel engine grunts
where pigs once hunted garbage.
A thin asthmatic cow shares the untrashed garage.

2   All that I can remember of his wife,
my father's mother, is that she sang us songs
('Great Tom is Cast' was one), that frightened me.
And she would go chug chugging with a jar
of milk until its white pap turned to yellow
butter. And in the basket underneath the stairs
she kept the polish for grandfather's shoes.

All that I have of her is voices:
laughing me out of fear because a crappaud
jumped and splashed the dark where I was huddled
in the galvanized tin bath; telling us stories
round her fat white lamp. It was her Queen
Victoria lamp, she said; although the stamp
read Ever Ready. And in the night, I listened to her singing
in a Vicks and Vapour Rub-like voice what you would call the
   blues

3   Come-a look
     come-a look
     see wha' happen

     come-a look
     come-a look
     see wha' happen

     Sookey dead
     Sookey dead
     Sookey dead-o

     Sookey dead
     Sookey dead
     Sookey dead-o

     Him a-wuk
     him a-wuk
     till'e bleed-o

     him a-wuk
     him a-wuk
     till'e bleed-o

     Sookey dead
     Sookey dead
     Sookey dead-o

     Sookey dead
     Sookey dead
     Sookey dead-o . . .

                          from *Islands* by EDWARD BRATHWAITE

As the clock struck one
The old man died.
He lay there,
Still,
Cold,
And white.
His wrinkled old face
And his still clear eyes,
No longer to see the world outside.

Then they gently placed him
In his own small coffin
Of white satin
And of silk,
With large brass handles.
And then they nailed him in.

The black hearse arrived
And the doors were opened.
Then four men
Dressed in black
Carried the coffin to the car,
And gently slid it in,
With the beautiful wreaths
Of carnations and roses
Placed on the top.
The hearse
Slowly
Moved.

Down the so familiar streets
Where he had so often walked
On summer days
And winter nights.
To end like this
In a big black hearse.

People stared
As they neared the church,
Wondering who had died.
Then the hearse stopped
Before the graveyard gates
And once again
He was carried upon high.

The hymns were sung,
And the prayers were said,
And they carried him outside
To a deep,
Dark, hole.
And gently they lowered him
Down,
And down.
Until at last
It came to rest
upon the hard black earth.

The blessing was said
As the priest
Sprinkled earth into the grave.
And as the people sobbed
And moved away
The grave was slowly filled.
And then the wreaths
Of beautiful flowers
Were placed upon the top
Until they perished,
And were thrown away.

PAULINE NORRIE, aged 12

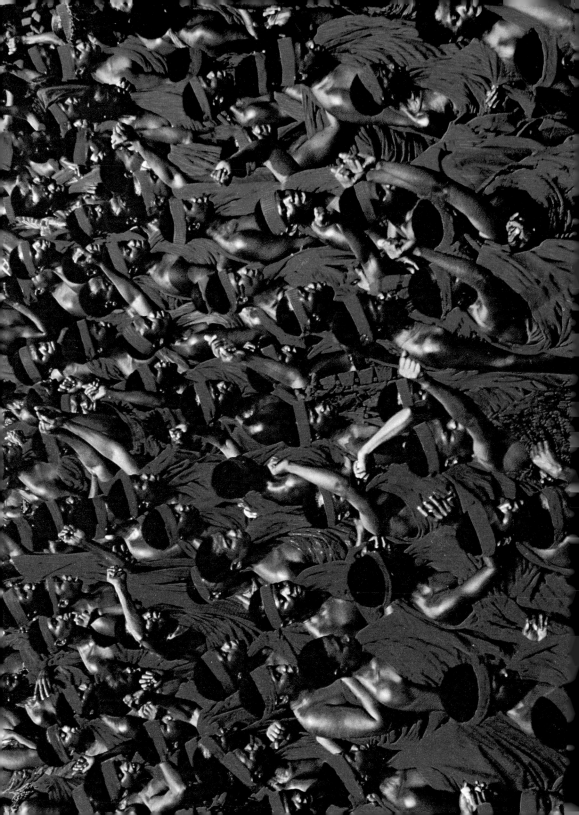

Jazz fantasia

Drum on your drums, batter on your banjoes,
sob on the long cool winding saxophones.
Go to it, O jazzmen.

Sling your knuckles on the bottoms of the happy
tin pans, let your trombones ooze, and go husha-
husha-hush with the slippery sandpaper.

Moan like an autumn wind high in the lonesome treetops, moan
    soft like
you wanted somebody terrible, cry like a racing car slipping
    away from a
motorcycle cop, bang-bang! you jazzmen, bang altogether
    drums, traps,
banjoes, horns, tin cans—make two people fight on the top of a
    stairway
and scratch each other's eyes in a clinch tumbling down the
    stairs.

Can the rough stuff . . . now a Mississippi steamboat pushes up
    the night
river with a hoo-hoo-hoo-oo . . . and the green lanterns calling
    to the high
soft stars . . . a red moon rides on the humps of the low river
    hills . . .
go to it, O jazzmen.

CARL SANDBURG

The blacksmith's boy went out with a rifle
and a black dog running behind.
Cobwebs snatched at his feet,
rivers hindered him,
thorn branches caught at his eyes to make him blind
and the sky turned into an unlucky opal,
but he didn't mind,
I can break branches, I can swim rivers, I can stare out any
   spider I meet,
said he to his dog and his rifle.

The blacksmith's boy went over the paddocks
with his old black hat on his head.
Mountains jumped in his way,
rocks rolled down on him,
and the old crow cried, You'll soon be dead.
And the rain came down like mattocks.
But he only said
I can climb mountains, I can dodge rocks, I can shoot an old
   crow any day,
and he went on over the paddocks.

When he came to the end of the day the sun began falling.
Up came the night ready to swallow him,
like the barrel of a gun,
like an old black hat,
like a black dog hungry to follow him.
Then the pigeon, the magpie and the dove began wailing
and the grass lay down to pillow him.
His rifle broke, his hat flew away and his dog was gone
and the sun was falling.

But in front of the night the rainbow stood on a mountain,
just as his heart foretold.
He ran like a hare,
he climbed like a fox;
he caught it in his hands, the colour and the cold—
like a bar of ice, like the column of a fountain,
like a ring of gold
The pigeon, the magpie and the dove flew up to stare,
and the grass stood up again on the mountain.

The blacksmith's boy hung the rainbow on his shoulder
instead of his broken gun.
Lizards ran out to see,
snakes made way for him,
and the rainbow shone as brightly as the sun.
All the world said, Nobody is braver, nobody is bolder,
nobody else has done
anything to equal it. He went home as bold as he could be
with the swinging rainbow on his shoulder.

JUDITH WRIGHT

Post office clerk

I queued in the Post Office—
It seemed endless, the waiting.
A large kangaroo was serving;
I watched him, for something to do.
He seemed very efficient, a long hop
Took him from end to end of the counter,
And his sloe eyes never blinked,
But always were pointed
Down his long nose
At the business he was about.
When my turn came, he was most polite,
And got what I wanted
With his deft paws.
I took my stamps and my change carefully, though.
What if the dark, wrinkled, clawed thing like a folded bat
Had brushed my hand as I reached beneath the grill?

MAY IVIMY

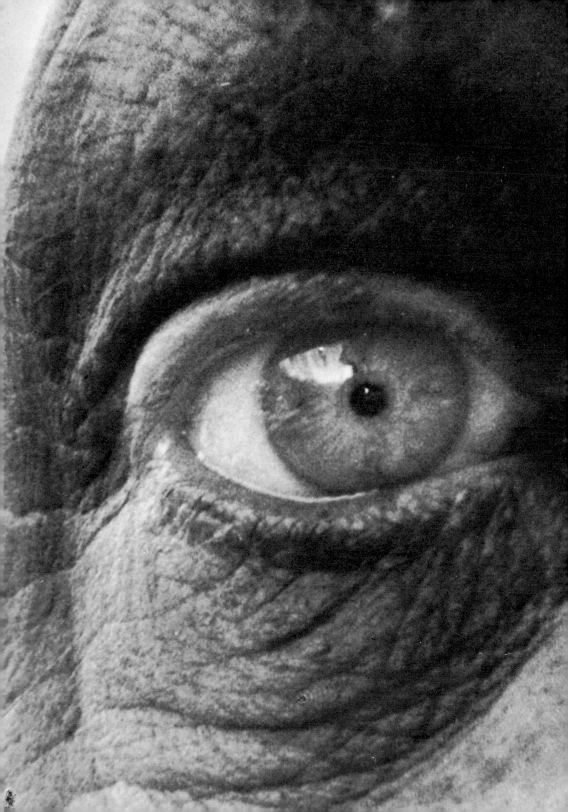

On cold nights
When the cold rain beats
And the wind howls,
On cold nights
When the cold snow falls
And the sleet swirls,
My only defence
Against that cold
Is to nibble black salt
And sip *sake* dregs.
But I finger my beard—
Scanty and starved—
Sniffle and cough,
And say to myself
'I'm a good fellow'—
Proud words, and empty:
I freeze all the same,
Swathing myself
In sheets made of sacking,
Piling on the top
My flimsy clothes.
The cold still seeps through.
But there are some
Poorer than I am,
Parents cold and hungry,
Womenfolk and children
Choking on tears.
On cold nights
How do *they* live?

103   Heaven and earth are broad,
So they say.
For me they are narrow.
Sun and moon are bright,
So they say.
They don't shine for me.
Is it the same for all men,
This sadness?
Or is it for me alone?
Chance made me man
And I, like any other, plough and weed.
But from my clothes—
Thin even when new—tatters hang down
Waving like seaweed.
In my rickety hovel the straw
Lies on bare earth.
By my pillow squat my parents,
At my feet my wife and children;
All huddled in grief.
From the hearth no smoke rises,
In the cauldron
A spider weaves its web.
How do you cook rice
When there is no rice left?
We talk feebly as birds.
And then, to make bad worse,
To snip the ends of a thread
Already frayed and short,
The village headman comes,
Shaking his whip in my face,
Shouting out for his tax,
Right at my pillow.

Is this the way things go?
Must it go on and on?
Yes. We are on earth.

Envoy
Earth is despair and shame.
But I am no bird, and I
Cannot escape from it.
                    YAMANOUE OKURA

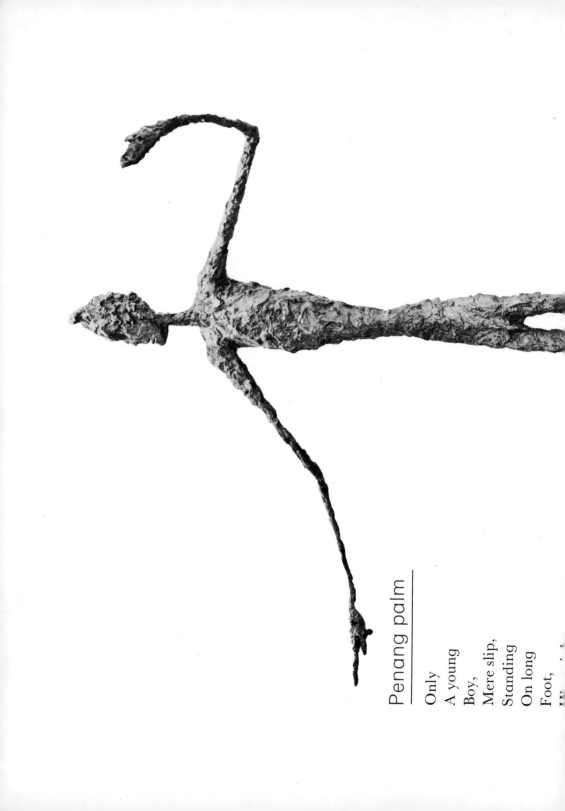

Penang palm

Only
A young
Boy,
Mere slip,
Standing
On long
Foot,

On still lip,
Leans,
Shaking
His wet mop
Of shaggy hair
Over the bare
Horizon sashed
With red, over
The beach
Where nets
Fret and fan
The frangipane's
Salted air,
Dreams
Of a fish,
In the breaking
Dawn
Stands and struts,
Shaking
A clutch of coconuts.
                        JAMES KIRKUP

Noah

When old Noah stared across the floods,
Sky and water melted into one
Looking-glass of shifting tides and sun.

Mountain-tops were few: the ship was foul:
All the morn old Noah marvelled greatly
At this weltering world that shone so stately,
Drowning deep the rivers and the plains.
Through the stillness came a rippling breeze;
Noah sighed, remembering the green trees.

Clear along the morning stooped a bird,—
Lit beside him with a blossomed sprig.
Earth was saved; and Noah danced a jig.

SIEGFRIED SASSOON

Night shapes

Outside is full of cats and darkness,
Howling screeches and thick black stillness,
Things creeping silently,
Bats shuddering restlessly,
Owls hooting,
Moles rooting.

Outside is full of black shapes moving,
Shadows weird and slowly passing,
Things watching the dark,
Eyes looking for work,
Figures stealing
Night brooding.

Outside is full of people dreaming,
Hoping, muttering, turning, scheming,
Ideas moving in the mind,
Voices uttering no sound
Time slipping,
Dawn looming.

PADDY KINSALE

A man

I knew a man, a common farmer, the father of five sons,
And in them the fathers of sons, and in them the fathers of sons.
This man was of wonderful vigour, calmness, beauty of person,
The shape of his head, the pale yellow and white of his hair and
  beard, the immeasurable meaning in his black eyes, the
  richness and breadth of his manners,
These I used to go and visit him to see, he was wise also,
He was six feet tall, he was over eighty years old, his sons were
  massive, clean, bearded, tan-faced, handsome,
They and his daughters loved him, all who saw him loved him,
They did not love him by allowance, they loved him with
  personal love,
He drank water only, the blood show'd like scarlet through the
  clear brown skin of his face,
He was a frequent gunner and fisher, he sail'd his boat himself,
  he had a fine one presented to him by a ship-joiner, he had
  fowling pieces presented to him by men that loved him,
When he went with his five sons and many grand-sons to hunt or
  fish, you would pick him out as the most beautiful and
  vigorous of the gang,
You would wish long and long to be with him, you would wish to
  sit by him in the boat that you and he might touch each other.

WALT WHITMAN

Man carrying bale

The tough hand closes gently on the load;
  Out of the mind, a voice
Calls 'Lift!' and the arms, remembering well their work,
  Lengthen and pause for help.
Then a slow ripple flows along the body,
While all the muscles call to one another:
  'Lift!' and the bulging bale
  Floats like a butterfly in June.

HAROLD MONRO

A gardener drinking tea

Gratefully gulping his hot cup of tea,
He belches and chokes,
And paddles the spoon round the edge of the cup
While he snatches a smoke.
As he rubs his cold nose on the sleeve of his coat
He sniffs, loosely and loud,
And, yawning, leans back on his damp, wooden seat,
With his grizzled head bowed.

GILLIAN, aged 13

Proletarian portrait

A big young bareheaded woman
in an apron

Her hair slicked back standing
on the street

One stockinged foot toeing
the sidewalk

Her shoe in her hand. Looking
intently into it

She pulls out the paper insole
to find the nail

That has been hurting her

WILLIAM CARLOS WILLIAMS

The sun shone strongly through the window
Lighting up the dancing particles of dust
Making mother's hair gleam
Like polished brass
Shining on her black shoes
On the red tiles
As she perched on the kitchen stool
Shelling peas.
Mother's hands are quick and deft
As they move from pod to pod
Throwing empty pods in one pile
And picking up a fresh one
From the brown paper bag
Like a fisherman, gutting fish.
As she splits the pod,
The green peas are revealed
Shining, like balls of green jade.
They cling to the pod
Like a child to its mother,
But unlike a child
They are parted at a touch
And patter, like green rain
On to the other peas below.
The green of the peas
Against the white of the bowl
Looks like green grass, peeping through the snow
At the beginning of a thaw
And as more peas patter down
It is as if the snow were melting, to reveal
A hill of green,

Each empty pod looks like
The green beak of some bird.
Empty, useless, soon to be thrown away
Their time of usefulness is done.
But all peas are wasted
As far as I'm concerned
Simply because . . . . . .
I don't like peas!

KATHERINE BOARD, aged 12

Aunt and uncle

I was staying at the time with my uncle and his wife. Although she was my aunt, I never thought of her as anything but the wife of my uncle, partly because he was so big and trumpeting and red-hairy and used to fill every inch of the hot little house like an old buffalo squeezed into an airing cupboard, and partly because she was so small and silk and quick and made no noise at all as she whisked about on padded paws, dusting the china dogs, feeding the buffalo, setting the mousetraps that never caught her; and once she sleaked out of the room, to squeak in a nook or nibble in the hayloft, you forgot she had ever been there.

But there he was, always, a steaming hulk of an uncle, his braces straining like hawsers, crammed behind the counter of the tiny shop at the front of the house, and breathing like a brass band; or guzzling and blustery in the kitchen over his gusty supper, too big for everything except the great black boats of his boots. As he ate, the house grew smaller; he billowed out over the furniture, the loud check meadow of his waistcoat littered, as though after a picnic, with cigarette ends, peeling, cabbage stalks, birds' bones, gravy; and the forest fire of his hair crackled among the hooked hams from the ceiling. She was so small she could hit him only if she stood on a chair, and every Saturday night at half past ten he would lift her up, under his arm, on to a chair in the kitchen so that she could hit him on the head with whatever was handy, which was always a china dog. On Sundays, and when pickled, he sang high tenor, and had won many cups.

from *A Prospect of the Sea* by DYLAN THOMAS

Eddie

He stood with Eddie Radford during playtime. 'I used to be a Protestant,' said Eddie. 'My father were a Cath'lic when he an' my mam got wed an' she were a Protestant. He didn't turn for her, but he let his own religion drop. I went to a Proddy school, Pink Lane, but me dad were a bomb-thrower in the Loyal North Lancs, an' he kept havin' visions an' things in the trenches, so he wrote to my mam for her to send me to the Cath'lic school, an' she didn't want to go against him, with him bein' in the trenches an' it might be his dying wish. So she sent me here. But when he came back all right after the war she were sorry. It costs a lot more bein' a Cath'lic, what wi' raffles for the church, collections, money at the church door, keeping the priests an' all that, an' then a new suit every year for Walking Day. You've got to pay two-an'-threepence for a new school cap once a year, an' my mam reckons you can get the same thing from the shop-with-the-man-at-the-door for ninepence. Here, feel at the top of my skull. Put thy hand on flat and press. Feel owt? Hollow, see. It's like a soup plate on the top of my head. Our Albert's responsible for that—he kept clouting me on the nut when I were a baby. It takes a full twelvemonth for the crust of a child's head to set, an' he kept smackin' me, an' it were a bit doughy, so when it set it set with this hollow in it. They say that if I were to head a football I could drop dead. I'll never forgive our Albert for that I won't. My mam still thinks Cath'lics worship statues. She'll not be told that they're only there to remind us. They have many a row, her an' my dad, about it.'

from *One Small Boy* by BILL NAUGHTON

Memories

When I was about nine we lived down by the river and there was one place where the water from the river formed a pool. Sometimes this pool was deep and sometimes it was shallow and then the sludge and the mud showed up through the water and the water got cloudy very easily. We sometimes still go and swim there in the hot weather but when I was younger I used to go there often because I lived quite close to it. One day I made a raft with two other boys. We had got part of an old shed wall with all the planks coming off it and the nails sticking out rusty. It was easy to nail all the planks down again and then we had got quite a big raft, big enough to lie down on. All we had to do then was to find a long enough pole to stick in the water. That didn't take long to find because I used my mother's prop. I sneaked it away because I knew she wouldn't miss it on a day she wasn't washing.

We got the raft afloat all right and pushed it out with the prop. There were two boys with me. Jackie Robinson and Billy Marsh. It was smashing on this raft on the pool because it was a big pool. We went right across the middle and then we got stuck in the mud. We tried to get off the raft and push it but we kept on sinking into the mud and we had to get back on to this raft and there was nothing we could do except wait for the pool to fill up so that we could get off again. We had to wait a long time and when I got back my mom played war with me because I'd still got her prop and it had got mud all over it. She said to me, 'If I ketch you on that pool again I'll give it you.' She always says that.

STEPHEN, aged 11

Guilty conscience

I went to the shed for a cigarette. Mind, I was not allowed to
   smoke, and if Dad caught me, there's no telling *what* would
   happen.

I lit it,
And puffed
What's that?
Quick as a flash the cigarette is out and I stand with beating
   heart, waiting.
It was only the door, swinging and creaking in the evening
   breeze.
I lit up again
And puffed.
The door opened with a push and a clatter, hitting, storming,
   searching out the sinner.
Without waiting to think, I dashed out, down the path round the
   corner, and indoors.
Safe?
Safe from myself?

RODNEY SIVYOUR

There was the time when I was stuck in the mango tree and could not get down. My mother had told me not to climb any more trees and warned me that the next time I did, I would suffer the consequences. I had tried to follow that rule, but a friend had dared me to climb this tree so I had to show him I was not chicken.

I eventually got down out of it by way of a ladder my brother propped up against the trees. I vowed never to climb another tree, but up to now I am still climbing trees.

WINSTON FOREST

First day

The morning came, without any warning, when my sisters surrounded me, wrapped me in scarves, tied up my boot-laces, thrust a cap on my head, and stuffed a baked potato in my pocket.

'What's this?' I said.

'You're starting school today.'

'I ain't. I'm stopping 'ome.'

'Now, come on, Loll. You're a big boy now.'

'I ain't.'

'You are.'

'Boo-hoo.'

They picked me up bodily, kicking and bawling, and carried me up to the road.

'Boys who don't go to school get put into boxes, and turn into rabbits, and get chopped up Sundays.'

I felt this was overdoing it rather, but I said no more after that. I arrived at the school just three feet tall and fatly wrapped in my scarves. The playground roared like a rodeo, and the potato burned through my thigh. Old boots, ragged stockings, torn trousers and skirts, went skating and skidding around me. The rabble closed in; I was encircled; grit flew in my face like shrapnel. Tall girls with frizzed hair, and huge boys with sharp elbows, began to prod me with hideous interest. They plucked at my scarves, spun me round like a top, screwed my nose, and stole my potato.

I was rescued at last by a gracious lady—the sixteen-year-old junior-teacher—who boxed a few ears and dried my face and led me off to The Infants. I spent that first day picking holes in paper, then went home in a smouldering temper.

'What's the matter, Loll? Didn't he like it at school, then?'

'They never gave me the present!'

'Present? What present?'

'They said they'd give me a present.'

'Well, now, I'm sure they didn't.'

'They did! They said: "You're Laurie Lee, ain't you? Well, just you sit there for the present." I sat there all day but I never got it. I ain't going back there again!'

But after a week I felt like a veteran and grew as ruthless as anyone else. Somebody had stolen my baked potato, so I swiped somebody else's apple.

from Cider with Rosie by LAURIE LEE

Fight

I remember when I first came to this school in England I was very unhappy because I was an outcast from the others. I just wanted to be friendly and have a good time with everybody but instead people were always calling after me because my skin is black. And I wanted to tell them that I could do anything they could do and play with them, like playing football or cricket, or running or playing hide-and-seek—any of those things I could do really well. And I was so miserable with them calling after me because I was black and they were white. And I wanted to leave that school more than anything in the world. I was always thinking, 'Maybe one day, I will get in a boat and sail away until I come to an Island where I can fight with the wild animals and be my own boss like Robinson Crusoe, but I knew I was only dreaming.

There was a big boy at this school who was worse than the

others calling after me and making my life miserable. His name was Macinley and because he was big he sure thought he could throw his weight around all over everybody. He was always picking on me and driving me mad. But I noticed that he picked on white boys as well, especially little ones that couldn't defend themselves. It used to make me mad thinking the way he did this. And another thing was that I knew the others wouldn't always be pushing me off if it wasn't for him. I could easily tell they were only saying those things to please him and make him think he was a great guy.

But one day I had enough of him. I was in the playground and I heard some noise round the corner. When I got there this Macinley was torturing a little white boy, pulling his hair and throwing his jacket about and making him fetch it and the little boy was crying. And Macinley said to me, 'What you think you're grinning at?' So I said, 'I'm not grinning at anything. And you should leave him alone. He's only a little boy. You want to try it on with someone your own size.' And he said, 'You want to try?' And then I rushed out at him mad and everybody was shouting. He hit me on the lip and made my lip bleed but I didn't take any notice of that, I wammed at him and beat him up real good so he was on the ground calling me to stop. I was so frightened I expected they would all set on me. But what happened? Everybody was cheering me, especially the girls and saying what a great guy I was to beat up Old Macinley the bully and stop him from torturing the little kid. And ever since then I've had lots of friends. We go off playing cricket, football, climbing and swimming at the baths and all kinds of things now. And we never have any trouble from the Macinley. He's learnt his lesson for good.

JOHN

School

After three o-clock playtime on the Wednesday, Miss Skegham began a poetry lesson. The class was divided into four seasons, and each one had to chant a verse suitable to the season.

'Sheed, let me hear you give Spring,' said Miss Skegham. 'The rest of the class silence.'

Sheed faced her, giving a whisper first, 'I'll spring you—,' and then opening the right side of his mouth: '"Summer is a-comin' in,"' he piped, '"loudly sing cuckoo."'

'Cuckoo,' she corrected.

'Cookoo, Cookoo,' he trilled.

He admired the boy's coolness. If she asks me, he thought, I'll drop dead. 'M'Cloud,' she called, 'let's hear "The North Wind" from you.'

He stood facing her and the circle of faces, his heart shaking, and praying mentally for help from the Virgin, he forced his dry voice out:

> '"The North wind doth blow,
>   And we shall have snow,
>   And what will the robin do then, poor ting?
>   He'll—"'

'*Ting?*' she repeated. 'Poor *ting?* Say "thing". Start from the beginning again. No need for you others to titter.'

Ting, thing, ting, thing? He cleared his throat but couldn't remember the opening. She said: '"The North wind doth blow ..."' He coughed. The blood felt up to his eyes. Ting? thing? He'd have to watch for that. 'Right,' she said. He began: '"The North wind doth blow. And we shall have snow, And what ..."' 'Not so fast,' she said. 'Go on. "And what ..."' '"And what, and what will the robin do then ..."' it was somewhere near and he'd have to watch out for it, they were all listening and watching him. 'Go on,' she said. He went on: '"And what will the robin do then, poor t-ting . . ."'

'Ting! ting!' she said and he heard them all snigger. 'Don't you know the King's English yet, M'Cloud?'

King's English—I'm Irish. She's saying that against the Irish. The flush died down and his face went cool. '*Thing*!' she called out, '*thing, thing, thing.* Class, say "poor thing".' They let out one loud, 'Poor thing'. 'Right, M'Cloud,' she said, in a rather kindly voice: 'Yes, "The North Wind . . ."' The nice touch in her voice almost started him, but not quite. 'M'Cloud,' she shouted, 'come on, "The North Wind . . ."'

He stood unbudging. He saw her eyes bulge and the redness swarm up her throat as she came up to him and gave him a swinging slap on the side of the head. It made things spin for a moment, but he didn't feel any pain, and he stood as erect as he could, feeling that half the side of his face was missing: 'Now will you say it?' she asked. He didn't speak. He could only half see her, for the spots were still jumping. 'Right,' she said, going for her cane. 'Hold out your hand.' He put his right hand out and she held up the cane. It came down clean across the palm. 'The other,' she said. He held out the left hand. The cane came down with a sharper rush. It made him tremble with pain. She waited a second: 'Now,' she said, 'we'll have "The North Wind doth blow."'

He stood there trying to stop all his body from shaking. The pain was simple to bear, but he longed for a calm moment to come to him. He didn't speak. She thrust her cane under his right armpit and nudged his arm out. She gave him a rap on it. Then she gave him a rap on the other hand. He hoped the tears wouldn't start. He found running through his mind the words, 'Brave

Robert Emmet, the darling of Erin, Brave Robert Emmet he died with a smile,' in answer to the King's English. The class had gone very silent. She said: 'Right, M'Cloud. Now we'll have "The North Wind doth blow . . ."' He felt the turn of heart inside him, and something in his mind said, you won't! It was all right now, that calm thing had come, and she could crucify him and he wouldn't cry, nor would he ever say 'The North Wind.'

He felt himself caught by the ear, and pulled up to the front of the class, just below her desk where she forced him down on his knees: 'Kneel there,' she said, 'and kneel up straight. Keep your hands behind your back. And tell me when you're ready to say "The North Wind . . ."' I'll stay here happily, he thought, till there's a hole in the ground.

It was a relief to kneel with face unseen by the other boys. Outside the bell in the corridor rang for afternoon catechism. Now that he was over his punishment he felt he wouldn't have been without it. He had to avoid thinking of his mother's face, because when he did the tears would come to his eyes in spite of himself. So he imagined himself taking long leaping strides all the way from home to school, and he counted them as he went along. And when his mother's face came he thought of Robert Emmet.

from *One Small Boy* by BILL NAUGHTON

Seventeen oranges

I used to be so fond of oranges that I could suck one after the other the whole day long—until that time the policeman gave me a scare at the dock gates when he caught me almost red-handed with seventeen hidden away in my various pockets, and he locked me up, and ever since then I've never looked at an orange—because that gave me my fill of them.

I was driving a little pony-and-cart for the Swift Delivery Company in those days, and lots of my pick-ups were at the docks, where I could put on a handy sample load and be back at the depot before the other carters had watered their mares.

Now I was not what you call a proper fiddler, and I did not make a practice of knocking things off just because they didn't belong to me, like some people do, but just the same, it was very rare I came off those docks without a bit of something to have a chew at during the day.

Say they were unloading a banana boat; well, I used to draw my little cart alongside. There were often loose bunches that had dropped off the main stalks. And when the chance came I would either make a quick grab, or some friendly foot would shove them towards me. Then I used to duck them out of sight under my brat. The brat was an apron made from a Tate and Lyle sugar bag, supposed to be a good protection against rain and rough wear, but mine was used mostly for concealment. And for the rest of the day I'd be munching away at bananas, even though I hadn't a passion for them like I had for oranges.

But mine was all done on the spur of the moment, more or less, and not worked out to a fine art, as in one instance with Clem Jones, who came out of the gates carrying a box.

'What have you got in there?' asked Pongo, who was the bobby on duty.

'A cat,' said Clem, 'but don't ask me to open it, or the blighter will get away.'

'A cat?' said Pongo. 'Don't come it. Let's have it opened.'

Clem wouldn't at first, but when Pongo insisted he got mad, and he flung it open, and out leapt a ship's cat, which darted back along the docks with Clem after it, shouting. Two minutes later he came out with the same box, holding the lid down tight and scowling at the grinning Pongo, and all the way home he scowled, until in the privacy of his own kitchen he opened the box and took out a full-sized Dutch cheese.

I got caught because the string of my brat broke, and Pongo, after looking over my head, noticed my somewhat bulging pockets. He made me draw the pony-and-cart to one side, and then he took me in his cabin and went through my pockets. There were seventeen oranges in all, and he placed them carefully on the table.

'An example has to be made,' he said, 'of somebody or other— and I reckon you're the unlucky one. Now, my lad, what have you to say for yourself?'

I said nothing. I was dead frightened, but I forced myself to keep my mouth shut. I had read too many detective stories to make the mistake of blabbing. *Anything you say may be used in evidence against you.* I kept that firm in my mind, and I refused to be interrogated. Pongo, who did not care for my attitude, said, 'Righto, I'll go off and bring a colleague as a witness.' And with that he went, carefully locking the door behind him.

I felt awful then. It was the suspense. I looked at the walls, I looked at the door, and I looked at the seventeen oranges, and I looked at my brat with the broken string. I thought of how I would get sacked and get sentenced, and of what my mother would say and my father do.

There was no escape. I was there—and the evidence was there before me on the table—and Pongo had gone for his mate to be witness. I was ruined for life.

'Oh, my God,' I moaned in anguish, 'whatever shall I do?'

'*Eat 'em!*' spoke a voice in my head.

'Eh?' I asked. 'Eat 'em?'

'*Yeh, that's right,*' replied this inner voice—'*and then the evidence will be gone. But be quick about it.*'

I thought for half a second—then I snatched an orange, peeled it in a jiff, popped it in my mouth, crushed the juice out and swallowed it, swallowing the orange, and I was just about to squirt out the pips when the voice cried:

'*No!*'

'Eh?'

'*You have to swallow them too!*'

'What—the pips?'

'*Yes—peel an' all! Evidence.*'

'Oh—oh, of course,' and I forced the pips to the back of my mouth and took a handful of peel to help get them down my gullet.

'*Don't bother to chew,*' said the voice, '*it's a race against time.*'

It certainly was. After the first orange I took out my penknife and slashed the fruit into chunks and gulped them down as fast as I could pick them up.

I was all but full to the brim, with three oranges still to go, when I heard Pongo and his mate coming back. With a sigh I gave up, but the voice warned me to guzzle on, suggesting that the more evidence I ate the less there would be—and as luck would have it, Pongo and his mate were detained over checking-up on some outgoing wagons, and since the sigh seemed to have cleared up a sort of traffic-jam in my oesophagus, I set about finishing off those last few, and by the time the key turned in the lock I was consuming the final piece of the seventeen oranges.

'This is him,' began Pongo to his mate, 'I caught him with his pockets ramjam full of oranges—' He looked to the table. 'Hi, where are they?'

'Whew,' sniffed his mate, 'I can smell 'em.'

I never spoke.

Pongo began to search. He looked high and low, went through my pockets, felt at my brat, but of course he found no trace of an orange. Finally he figured out what must have happened, but even he couldn't believe it. '*Seventeen oranges*,' he kept murmuring—'big 'uns at that!—how has he managed it?' But I said nothing. And he couldn't give me in charge, because he had no evidence upon which to commit me—and because I suppose he did not want to be laughed at. So all he could do was to vituperate, while I kept my lips shut tight, and then he had to let me go.

When I told Clem Jones about it he said that I had been very slow; he said that I could have sued Pongo for hundreds of pounds because of wrongful detention, if only I had been quick-witted enough. But I never was a vindictive sort, and anyway, it was days and days before I could stand really still and think things out, because those seventeen oranges—peel, pips, and all—kept working away in my inside something shocking.

from *The Goalkeeper's Revenge* by BILL NAUGHTON

Under the pier

High up among the girders of the pier,
Under the dark planking of the pier,
They perch and sing:
A boy with tarry legs, and lower,
A girl in blue jeans.
Suddenly he leans—
Heedless of us beneath him,
Heedless of twisted ankle and broken bones—
And with a whoop comes clattering down among the stones.

JOHN WALSH

The dress

Like all very plain little girls Margie knew there lurked inside
her a beautiful princess just waiting to be released. She sat huddled
over her book, shoulders rounded, straight black hair falling over
her eyes, oblivious of the smallness and meanness of the terrace
house where she lived with her Gran and Grandad, sailing in a
dream ship over emerald oceans, drawn in a golden shell by white
swans to fairyland, where warmth and joy and happy ever after
awaited her . . .

'That bairn reads too much,' her Grandad's rough voice broke
through. 'Ought to be out playing. Get some colour in 'er cheeks.
Come on, Mick,' he said to her, using his funny pet name for her.

'Get thi' ball, an' we'll have a game in t' street.'

Resigned, Margie put down her book, and for ten minutes the old man enjoyed a romp, throwing, catching, chasing, whilst the child with fumbling fingers but nimble thoughts turned the ball to gold, the cobbled street into a gracious court, and transformed the workman's blue overalls into livery of gleaming splendour, until her Gran called them in for a dinner of mash and sausages.

As she constructed mountains, chasms, rivers and roads in the piled potatoes, making gravy waterfalls, her grandparents planned the afternoon. 'Regal? Odeon? St. George's?' 'It's a musical at t'Tower, an' coloured,' said Gran. So it was settled. A bag of Maltesers, a packet of fags and a Barley Sugar stick from Coxe's and they were off to join the queue for the one and nine's; those, and the warm dark, the plush seats and the flashlights were part of every Saturday afternoon, but today, somehow, was special. As they stumbled into their seats there *she* was on the screen—riding in a black carriage in a white dress and huge straw hat, and singing with clear high notes, smiling—so beautiful, so perfect. The child was dizzy with admiration and so captivated as the trivially romantic story came to its inevitable ending that she hardly moved a muscle except when the tears of joy and sorrow made long streams down her cheeks and had to be secretly wiped from her chin with the back of her hand.

As they walked home in the gathering dusk she relived every scene, especially the one where *she* wore that dark green dress, all down to the floor and glittering with diamonds at the neck, her shoulders all bare, and she just *looked*. Didn't even sing at all.

'Sentimental rubbish!' said Grandad over her head.

'Well, I enjoyed it, and you did as well, didn't you pet?' said her Grandmother. But there was no answer from the little girl.

Radiant in that green velvet dress, eyes firmly closed against the reality of Market Street, Margie was whirling round and round a marble ball room in the arms of a dark-eyed hero, singing like an angel. Just like Deanna on the screen.

A few days later Margie came dashing in from Brownies, her eyes burning with excitement.

'We're having a fancy dress, Gran,' she said breathlessly. 'We can go as anything, we have to make it ourselves and it's in two weeks and I'm going to make a dress all stuck out like an old-fashioned lady, and can I? Please, Gran, please?'

'Now that'll take a bit of doing,' said Gran. 'Where do you think we're going to find anything like that?' The child's face fell. 'Well, I'll see what I can look out, pet. I expect we'll manage something. But you mustn't be too disappointed if . . .' Her voice trailed away for the child had disappeared, rushing off to the book she had put down before she had been forced into her brown tunic and cap two hours before.

The next day as she went to school the child entertained her companions with details of the marvellous dress she was going to wear to the fancy dress party. The picture in her head was so complete that no doubt as to the certainty of having the dress occurred. It already existed—she could feel the softness of the velvet, hear the swish as she walked in it. As the days wore on the rest of the children became just as convinced as she was. But then Gran said that they couldn't really do it. Where was the fine velvet to come from, who was to make such a dress? There was a war on and you couldn't get things, too difficult, coupons, waste . . . the reasons followed one on top of another. But none of it touched the child's mind. There *was* a dress; she knew it. Somehow she was sure she had seen it. She wandered out down the street and into

Layerthorpe and over the rubble of Hungate. There were the remains of demolished houses there and you could find treasures like bits of marble for hopscotch, coloured patterned tiles, broken glass glittering like jewels, and flowers and weeds grew over the remains of walls and stone steps. As she sat there in her misery, Margie became aware of Kath. Kath went to Brownies too but not the same school.

'Wot you goin' as?' she said.

'Not goin'.' Margie sulked miserably.

'Why not?'

'Can't get a frock.'

'My mam's got 'undreds,' said Kath. 'We got a shop. An' shoes to match. I'm goin' Japanese with a umbrella like paper.'

'Parasol,' corrected Margie. Kath sat down.

'You can have a frock off me mam if you like,' she said pulling her hair over her head and tucking the ends into her mouth. 'What sort you want?'

Out flowed the description, every detail of it embellished as it grew in the child's mind.

'We got one like that, I think,' said Kath. 'Green, soft. Ever so smooth.'

'Is it tight here?' said Margie, her hands on her flat child's chest and waist. 'And long and wide at the bottom, and bare here and here, and no sleeves—well, only a bit—and glittery?' Her voice grew to a squeak with growing hope and excitement.

'Yes,' said Kath. 'You can 'ave it. I'll ask me mam, anyway,' she added with a little caution. 'Tell you what. I'll meet you here tomorrow and tell you definite.'

Margie ran home elated.

'Nell,' said Grandad. 'It don't seem right to me. I only hope it's true . . . You know what kids are. Mick, are you listening to me? You mustn't depend on it, now. Her mam might say no. It mightn't fit. Who is 'er, anyway?'

'*Kath*, I told you,' said Margie patiently. Of course it would be all right—that was only old Granda'. It always is in the stories, she told herself.

The next afternoon she was already on the sun-warmed stone when Kath arrived.

'Okay,' she said. 'Come on, if yer comin'.'

Together they ran over the rubble, through an alley and down into narrow streets full of old and rather dilapidated houses and shops. One had three balls hanging over the door and Kath stopped. 'Here,' she said.

The window was a jumble of objects—china dogs, shabby shoes, jewellery pinned on old cardboard, candlesticks, jugs, and a row of old coats, dresses, suits on coathangers filled the back of the window.

'Come on in, then,' said Kath, and the doorbell jangled. A thin, tired woman stood behind a high counter.

'Hello, pet,' she said, handing over a parcel. 'No good to me. Got it in a job lot. Put in t' shoes as well. Be a bit of fun I expect. You' mam'll have to turn it up a bit. Run along now. Kath's got to get 'er tea.'

The parcel was wrapped in newspaper and thin, knotted string. Margie didn't know why but she suddenly felt sick. The shop had a bad smell and was dark. She grabbed the parcel.

'Thank you very much,' she said, and ran. She didn't stop until she came to the stone step where she sat down and untied the string with trembling fingers. Out fell the frock—green, satin, unevenly faded to a sickly yellowy white. A few sequins still clung to the deep V neck and the bias-cut skirt drooped grotesquely. There were frills at the shoulders instead of sleeves, and where she had imagined the wide hooped skirt hung the limp, creased folds. The shoes, died to match, had dirty scuffed toes and sequins stuck on the anklestraps. Silently, the child rewrapped the parcel. She searched around the rubble for a slate and began to scratch in the earth where it was softer, slowly at first and then with a mounting panic. Then, when the hole was deep enough, she buried the parcel, covering it over with the loosened earth, and then piling on bricks and stones. She walked slowly back home.

'Well, what happened? Have you got it?' asked Gran.

'No.' Unable to face the truth of that green horror of a dress, she lied: 'Her mam wouldn't let me have it.'

'I knew it!' said Gran angrily, and then she hugged the child. 'Never mind, pet. We'll think of something. Come and eat your tea. It's potted meat from Wright's. You like that, and Auntie Jinny popped in wi' some books for you. They're old, but she got 'em at a sale an' she knows you like to read.'

After tea Margie turned for consolation to the books. 'Angela Brazil,' she read. 'Oh, I like these. All about boarding schools and poor girls making good and . . .' She read on as her Gran began to clear away the tea-things and then to tidy up the grate. She became absorbed in the story. It was just like a miracle! She could hardly believe her eyes, for in the story the poor companion on the cruise-liner had to go to a fancy dress party and had nothing to wear. As everyone dressed up in expensive costumes she was in despair. And there before Margie lay the answer. It wasn't beautiful but it was easy and the party *was* tomorrow . . .

Gran managed to get everything needed the next day.

'Thank goodness everything's not rationed,' she said, as

Grandad and she measured and cut and glued. 'Now, you just go steady,' they told Margie, as they buttoned her into her coat. 'Or you'll tear.'

She called for Thelma and Mary on the way, and the twins. They were curious and a little contemptuous.

'Where's you' long frock, then? Thought it wer green velvet? You always did show off, Margie Woods.' But the girl crackled on wordlessly. At Brownies she took off her coat.'

'I'm a parcel!' she announced defiantly, in her brown paper, string, sealing-wax, old stamps, tie-on lable and all.

'What happened to that dress?' asked Mary, but even to her dearest friend she couldn't admit the truth.

'They said I'd spoil it, larking about,' she said, and skipped away to dance around the toadstool.

She won first prize. She knew she would—it happened in the story, and Margie had faith in Literature.

She came forward to Brown Owl who put round her neck a beautiful necklace.

'It's real crystals,' she said, 'so take good care of it.' The necklace flashed with rainbows much admired by all. But her friends basked in reflected glory as they walked home, each begging for a chance to hold the treasure just a moment to see the colours for themselves.

That night, as she undressed she stood in her vest in front of the dressing-table with the crystals round her neck, pulled the artificial silk bedspread from the bed and draped herself grandly in front of the mirror in a splendid dramatic pose.

'Just like Deanna Durbin in the picture,' said Gran as she came into the bedroom. 'Now into bed with you.'

JOAN GUEST

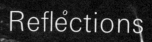

Reflections

Mirror, mirror!

Mirror, Mirror, tell me plain
Am I pretty or plain,
Or am I downright ugly
And ugly to remain?

Shall I marry a gentleman?
Shall I marry a clown?
Or shall I marry old Knives and Scissors
Shouting through the town?

ROBERT GRAVES

There is a time between night and day when landscapes sleep. Only the earliest riser sees that hour; or the all-night traveller, letting up the blind of his railway-carriage window, will look out on a rushing landscape of stillness, in which trees and bushes and plants stand immobile and breathless in sleep—wrapped in sleep, as the traveller himself wrapped his body in his great-coat or his rug the night before.

This grey still hour before morning was the time in which Tom walked into his garden. He had come down the stairs and along the hall to the garden door at midnight; but when he opened that door and stepped out into the garden, the time was much later. All night—moonlit or swathed in darkness—the garden had stayed awake; now, after that night-long vigil, it had dozed off.

The green of the garden was greyed over with dew; indeed, all its colours were gone until the touch of sunrise. The air was still, and the tree shapes crouched down upon themselves. One bird spoke; and there was a movement when an awkward parcel of feathers dislodged itself from the fir-tree at the corner of the lawn, seemed for a second to fall and then at once was swept up and along, outspread, on a wind that never blew, to another, farther tree: an owl. It wore the ruffled, dazed appearance of one who has been up all night.

from *Tom's Midnight Garden* by PHILIPPA PEARCE

I

On a Saturday afternoon in the football season,
I lie in a bed near the lake,
And dream of moles with golden wings.

While the depth of the water trembles on the ceiling,
Like the tail of an enraged bird,
I watch the dust floating above the bed, content.

I think of ships leaving lonely harbours,
Dolphins playing far at sea,
Fish with the faces of old men come in from a blizzard.

II

A dream of moles with golden wings
Is not so bad; it is like imagining
Waterfalls of stone deep in mountains,
Or a wing flying alone beneath the earth.

I know that far out in the Minnesota lake
Fish are nosing the mouths of cold springs,
Whose water causes ripples in the sleeping sand,
Like a spirit moving in a body.

It is Saturday afternoon. Crowds are gathered,
Warmed by the sun, and the pure air.
I thought of this strange mole this morning,
After sleeping all night by the lake.

ROBERT BLY

It was high summer, and the boy was lying in the corn. He was happy because he had no work to do and the weather was hot. He heard the corn sway from side to side above him, and the noise of the birds who whistled from the branches of the trees that hid the house. Lying flat on his back he stared up into the unbrokenly blue sky falling over the edge of the corn. The wind, after the warm rain before noon, smelt of rabbits and cattle. He stretched himself like a cat, and put his arms behind his head. Now he was riding on the sea, swimming through the golden corn waves, gliding along the heavens like a bird; in seven-league boots he was springing over the fields; he was building a nest in the sixth of the seven trees that waved their hands from a bright green hill. Now he was a boy with tousled hair, rising lazily to his feet, wandering out of the corn to the strip of river by the hillside. He put his fingers in the water, making a mock sea-wave to roll the stones over and shake the weeds; his fingers stood up like ten tower pillars in the magnifying water, and a fish with a wise head and a lashing tail swam in and out of the tower gates.

from *A Prospect of the Sea* by DYLAN THOMAS

He is a sad dragon waiting his chance;
He waits for the world to change again.
His ancestors were the kings of the earth
And he watches with his beady eye
For something to fall out of the sky
So that he can roam about free
Like the dinosaurs from out of the sea.

MARK, aged 11

A small dragon

I've found a small dragon in the woodshed.
Think it must have come from deep inside a forest
because it's damp and green and leaves
are still reflecting in its eyes.

I fed it on many things, tried grass,
the roots of stars, hazel-nut and dandelion,
but it stared up at me as if to say, I need
foods you can't provide.

It made a nest among the coal,
not unlike a bird's but larger,
it is out of place here
and is quite silent.

If you believed in it I would come
hurrying to your house to let you share my wonder,
but I want instead to see
if you yourself will pass this way.

BRIAN PATTEN

The jungle in the mind

I thought I might go into the forest
Into the jungle of little light and much darkness
Where many animals skulk and scuttle in shadows deep.

But I was too young and anyway lived in a city
By a sacred river. And now the jungle is far away.
So in my mind I wander in a jungle dark.

In the mind is a forest. If you close your eyes
You can just see—there! A dazzling brilliant
Is a golden snake scuttling into the dark.

What food is he looking for? A small creature
Full of blood to swallow down, or a wary man?
Waiting to see what will happen. He can lie on a branch all day.

The snake is free, and so are the other animals
Who wander about in the silent forest.
Perhaps a tiger will come treading on soft paws

Concealing himself gently in the shadows to wait.
There is no rush for him. If he wishes he will leap out
Fiercely flash his fire, or be still unmoving.

And now then above the tiger's head the monkeys
They are the jabbering ones, the frisking ones
They do not care about the silence.

Nor do they care to disturb the tiger
Even when he looks up and growls his snarling teeth
They make fun of him high up, laughing back.

Now it is time to turn away from the jungle
In the mind and look back at outside things
Leaving the snake, the tiger and the others in the dark.

VIQUAR TARIQ, aged 11

Little Johnny takes a trip to another planet

Through his bedroom window, later they confirmed
Johnny drifted one Monday evening
Up above the sleeping world.

He left this message:

I've taken a trip to another planet
And I'll be away for a while,
so don't send the Escaped Children Squad after me
the Universe is too wild.

Now among black glass trees
he weaves intricate shapes
in a world an inch away from ours,
and from behind his eyes
he sees into a waiting room of light
and maps out the route dawn takes through
the nurseries of night.

He has switched on a world and walked inside;
and as silence blooms among the flowers
he wonders at people groping
through transparent hours.
He's found the perfect loophole:
sits on the other side,
a child with eyes as big as planets
whose dreams do not collide
with any forms of teaching
with any form of lies.

So don't send the Escaped Children Squad after him
he'll be away for a while,
he's taken a trip to another planet
and the Universe is too wild
for him to make it back
in the same state of mind.

BRIAN PATTEN

The fun they had

Margie even wrote about it that night in her diary. On the page headed 17 May, 2155, she wrote, 'Today Tommy found a real book!'

It was a very old book. Margie's grandfather once said that when he was a little boy *his* grandfather told him that there was a time when all stories were printed on paper.

They turned the pages, which were yellow and crinkly, and it was awfully funny to read words that stood still instead of moving the way they were supposed to—on a screen, you know. And then, when they turned back to the page before, it had the same words on it that it had had when they read it the first time.

'Gee,' said Tommy, 'what a waste. When you're through with the book, you just throw it away, I guess. Our television screen must have had a million books on it and it's good for plenty more. I wouldn't throw *it* away.'

'Same with mine,' said Margie. She was eleven and hadn't seen as many telebooks as Tommy had. He was thirteen.

She said, 'Where did you find it?'

'In my house.' He pointed without looking, because he was busy reading. 'In the attic.'

'What's it about?'

'School.'

Margie was scornful. 'School? What's there to write about school?' Margie always hated school, but now she hated it more than ever. The mechanical teacher had been giving her test after test in Geography and she had been doing worse and worse until her mother had shaken her head sorrowfully and sent for the County Inspector.

He was a round little man with a red face and a whole box of tools with dials and wires. He smiled at her and gave her an apple, then took the teacher apart. Margie had hoped he wouldn't know how to put it together again, but he knew how all right and after an hour or so, there it was again, large and black and ugly with a big screen on which all the lessons were shown and the questions were asked. That wasn't so bad. The part she hated most was the slot where she had to put homework and test papers. She always had to write them out in a punch code they made her learn when she was six years old, and the mechanical teacher calculated the mark in no time.

The inspector had smiled after he was finished and patted her head. He said to her mother, 'It's not the little girl's fault, Mrs Jones. I think the Geography sector was geared a little too quick. Those things happen sometimes. I've slowed it up to an average ten-year level. Actually, the overall pattern of her progress is quite satisfactory.' And he patted Margie's head again.

Margie was disappointed. She had been hoping they would take the teacher away altogether. They had once taken Tommy's teacher away for nearly a month because the History sector had blanked out completely.

So she said to Tommy, 'Why would anyone write about school?'

Tommy looked at her with very superior eyes. 'Because it's not our kind of school, stupid. This is the old kind of school that they had hundreds and hundreds of years ago.' He added loftily, pronouncing the word carefully, '*Centuries* ago.'

Margie was hurt. 'Well, I don't know what kind of school they had all that time ago.' She read the book over his shoulder for a while, then said, 'Anyway, they had a teacher.'

'Sure they had a teacher, but it wasn't a *regular* teacher. It was a man.'

'A man? How could a man be a teacher?'

'Well, he just told the boys and girls things and gave them homework, and asked them questions.'

'A man isn't smart enough.'

'Sure he is. My father knows as much as my teacher.'

'He can't. A man can't know as much as a teacher.'

'He knows almost as much, I betcha.'

Margie wasn't prepared to dispute that. She said, 'I wouldn't want a strange man in my house to teach me.'

Tommy screamed with laughter, 'You don't know much, Margie. The teachers didn't live in the house. They had a special building and all the kids went there.'

'And all the kids learned the same thing?'

'Sure, if they were the same age.'

'But my mother says a teacher has to be adjusted to fit the mind of each boy and girl it teaches and that each kid has to be taught differently.'

'Just the same they didn't do it that way then. If you won't like it, you don't have to read the book.'

'I didn't say I didn't like it,' Margie said quickly. She wanted to read about those funny schools.

They weren't even half finished when Margie's mother called, 'Margie! School!'

Margie looked up. 'Not yet, mamma.'

'Now,' said Mrs Jones. 'And its probably time for Tommy, too.'

Margie said to Tommy, 'Can I read the book some more with you after school?'

'Maybe,' he said, nonchalantly. He walked away whistling, the dusty old book tucked beneath his arm.

Margie went into the schoolroom. It was right next to her bedroom, and the mechanical teacher was on and waiting for her. It was always on at the same time every day except Saturday and Sunday, because her mother said little girls learned better if they learned at regular hours.

The screen was lit up, and it said: 'Today's arithmetic lesson is on the addition of proper fractions. Please insert yesterday's homework in the proper slot.'

Margie did so with a sigh. She was thinking about the old schools they had when her grandfather's grandfather was a little boy. All the kids from the whole neighbourhood came, laughing and shouting in the school-yard, sitting together in the schoolroom, going home together at the end of the day. They learned the same things so they could help one another on the homework and talk about it.

And the teachers were people . . .

The mechanical teacher was flashing on the screen: 'When we add the fractions $\frac{1}{2}$ and $\frac{1}{4}$—'

Margie was thinking about how the kids must have loved it in the old days. She was thinking about the fun they had.

from *Earth is Room Enough* by ISAAC ASIMOV

List of Illustrations

Acknowledgements

The author gratefully acknowledges permission to reproduce extracts from the following copyright works:
J. Redwood Anderson: 'The Train' from *The Bridge.* Reprinted by permission of Sidgwick & Jackson Ltd.;
Isaac Asimov: *Earth is Room Enough.* Copyright © 1967 by Isaac Asimov. Reprinted by permission of Doubleday
& Company Inc.; **Patricia Beer:** 'Lemmings' from *Just like the Resurrection.* Reprinted by permission of Macmillan
London and Basingstoke. **Robert Bly:** 'Laziness and Silence' from *Silence in the Snowy Fields.* Copyright © 1962 by
Robert Bly. Reprinted by permission of the author and Jonathan Cape Ltd.; **Edward Brathwaite:** 'South'
from *Rights of Passage.* Copyright © 1967 by Oxford University Press; 'Ancestors' from *Islands.* Copyright © 1969
by Oxford University Press. Reprinted by permission of the publishers; **Richard Church:** *The Cave* (William
Heinemann Ltd.). Reprinted by permission of Laurence Pollinger Ltd.; A. B. Clegg (editor). **'The Fire' and
'The Furnace'**, each by a boy aged 11, from *The Excitement of Writing.* Reprinted by permission of the County
Council of the West Riding of Yorkshire and Chatto & Windus Ltd.; **Kevin Crossley-Holland:** 'The Ruin'
from *The Battle of Maldon and Other Anglo-Saxon Poems.* Reprinted by permission of the Macmillan Company of
Canada and Macmillan London and Basingstoke; **Gerald Durrell:** *The Overloaded Ark.* Reprinted by permission
of Faber and Faber Ltd.; Boris Ford (editor). **'A Gardener Drinking Tea by Gillian** from *Young Writers,
Young Readers.* Reprinted by permission of the Hutchinson Publishing Group Ltd.; **William Golding:** *Lord of
the Flies.* Reprinted by permission of Faber and Faber Ltd.; **Robert Graves:** 'Mirror, Mirror!' from *Poems
1914–1926* (William Heinemann Ltd.). Reprinted by permission of A. P. Watt & Son on behalf of the author;
Stephen Hart: 'Machines that Die' from *Following the Sun* edited by Leonard Clark (Odhams Press Ltd.). Reprinted by permission of the Hamlyn Publishing Group Ltd.; **Seamus Heaney:** 'The Trout' from *Death of a
Naturalist.* Reprinted by permission of Faber and Faber Ltd.; **Ted Hughes:** 'Relic' from *Lupercal.* Reprinted by
permission of Faber and Faber Ltd.; **May Ivimy:** 'Post Office Clerk' from *Workshop New Poetry* issue no. 8. Reprinted by permission of Workshop Press Ltd.; **Paddy Kinsale:** 'Island', 'Horses', and 'Night Shapes'. Reprinted
by permission of the author; **Rudyard Kipling:** 'The Secret of the Machines' from *The Definitive Edition of Rudyard
Kipling's Verse* (Macmillan). Reprinted by permission of A. P. Watt & Son on behalf of Mrs. George Bambridge;
James Kirkup: 'Penang Palm' from *Refusal to Conform* (Oxford University Press). Reprinted by permission of
the author; **D. H. Lawrence:** *Phoenix* (William Heinemann Ltd.) and 'Humming Bird' from *The Complete Poems
of D. H. Lawrence* (William Heinemann Ltd.). Reprinted by permission of Laurence Pollinger Ltd. on behalf of
the Estate of the Late Mrs. Frieda Lawrence; **Laurie Lee:** *Cider with Rosie.* Reprinted by permission of the Hogarth
Press Ltd.; **Barry Maybury** (editor): 'When I was about nine' by Stephen and 'He is a sad dragon' by Mark
from *Creative Writing for Juniors.* Reprinted by permission of B. T. Batsford Ltd.; **Harold Monro:** 'Man Carrying
Bale'. Reprinted by permission of Gerald Duckworth & Co. Ltd.; **Bill Naughton:** *One Small Boy* (MacGibbon
and Kee). Reprinted by permission of Granada Publishing Ltd.; **Bill Naughton:** *The Goalkeeper's Revenge.*
Reprinted by permission of George G. Harrap & Company Ltd.; **Liam O'Flaherty:** 'The Rockfish' from *The
Short Stories of Liam O'Flaherty.* Reprinted by permission of Jonathan Cape Ltd.; **Yamanoue Okura:** 'Dialogue
on Poverty' from *The Penguin Book of Japanese Verse* translated by Geoffrey Bownas and Anthony Thwaite. Copyright
© 1964 by Geoffrey Bownas and Anthony Thwaite. Reprinted by permission of Penguin Books Ltd.; **Brian
Patten:** 'A Small Dragon' from *Notes to the Hurrying Man* and 'Little Johnny Takes a Trip to Another Planet'
from *Johnny's Confession.* Reprinted by permission of George Allen & Unwin Ltd.; **Philippa Pearce:** *Tom's Midnight
Garden.* Reprinted by permission of Oxford University Press; **A. K. Ramanujan:** 'Snakes' from *The Striders.*
Copyright © 1966 by Oxford University Press. Reprinted by permission of the publishers; **John Rathe:** 'The
Station' from *Miracles* edited by Richard Lewis. Copyright © 1966 by Richard Lewis. Reprinted by permission of
Penguin Books Ltd. and Simon & Schuster Inc.; **Michael Roberts:** 'In the Strange Isle' from *Collected Poems.*
Reprinted by permission of Faber and Faber Ltd.; **Carl Sandburg:** 'Jazz Fantasia' from *Smoke and Steel.* Copyright
© 1920 by Harcourt Brace Jovanovich, Inc., renewed 1948 by Carl Sandburg. 'Old Deep Sing-Song' from
Wind Song. Copyright © 1958 by Carl Sandburg. Reprinted by permission of Harcourt Brace Jovanovich, Inc.;
Siegfried Sassoon: 'Noah' from *Collected Poems* (Faber and Faber Ltd.). Reprinted by permission of Mr. G. T.
Sassoon; **Christopher Searle:** 'Boys' from *Workshop New Poetry* issue no. 13. Reprinted by permission of Workshop
Press Ltd.; **Jon Silkin:** 'Death of a Bird' from *Poems New and Selected.* Reprinted by permission of Chatto & Windus
Ltd.; **Rodney Sivyour:** 'Guilty Conscience' from *Let the Children Write* by Margaret Langdon. Reprinted by
permission of the Longman Group; **John Steinbeck:** *Cannery Row.* Reprinted by permission of William Heinemann
Ltd. and the Viking Press Inc., N.Y.; **Dylan Thomas:** *A Prospect of the Sea.* Reprinted by permission of J. M. Dent
& Sons Ltd. on behalf of the Trustees for the Copyrights of the late Dylan Thomas; **John Walsh:** 'Under the Pier'
from *The Roundabout by the Sea* (Oxford University Press). Reprinted by permission of the author; **Keith Waterhouse:** 'Proletarian
Portrait from *The Collected Earlier Poems* (MacGibbon & Kee Ltd.). Copyright © 1938 by William Carlos Williams.
Reprinted by permission of Laurence Pollinger Ltd. and New Directions Publishing Corporation, New York;
Judith Wright: 'Legend' from *The Gateway.* Reprinted by permission of Angus & Robertson (U.K.) Ltd.; **Han
Yu:** 'A Withered Tree' from *Poems by the Late T'ang* translated by A. C. Graham. Copyright © 1965 by A. C.
Graham. Reprinted by permission of Penguin Books Ltd.; **Kinoshita Yuji:** 'Late Summer' and Kambara
Yumei: 'Oyster Shell' both from *The Penguin Book of Japanese Verse* translated by Geoffrey Bownas and Anthony
Thwaite. Copyright © 1964 by Geoffrey Bownas and Anthony Thwaite. Reprinted by permission of Penguin
Books Ltd.
The author would also like to thank the following for permission to reprint their poems and prose pieces:
The Daily Mirror Children's Literary Competition for 'Suburbs' by Charles Martin, 'Mother Shelling Peas' by
Katherine Board. S. Freeman and The Director of Education, Walsall, Katherine Tyrrell, Lesley, Stephanie
Alliss, Terry and Birmingham Education Department, Rosemary Bromley, Helen, Wendy Maggs, Pauline
Norrie, Winston Forest, John, Joan Guest and Viquar Tariq.